Free and Inexpensive Materials for Preschool and Early Childhood

Second Edition

Robert Monahan
Morehead State University
Morehead, Kentucky

FEARON PUBLISHERS, INC.
Belmont, California

*to Dr. Nona Burress . . . a humanist
who shares her experiences and love
through education.*

Contents

Introduction

I am pleased to bring you the second edition of this book. Many exciting new sources of materials are added to sources revised from the first edition. Materials are available only from the listed distributors, not from the author or publisher. These distributors have assured me that they have supplies ample for the next two years; however, because inflation has affected the publishing industry, the prices given are approximate and are subject to change without notice. The information concerning each item has been verified by its distributor.

To make clear which items are for use directly with children, such entries are marked with an asterisk (*). Items not so marked are intended as background or resource material for adults involved with children.

I would especially like to thank the persons who contributed to the preparation of this book. Special recognition is given to Deborah Cornett, Debi McLaughlin, and to my wife Sue and my daughter Amy Leigh.

Robert Monahan, *Editor*

How to Order Materials

Whenever possible, orders for materials should be written on school or organizational stationery. You should mention that the item was listed in this book.

To order, give the exact title and the number of the item you desire. Print or type your full name and address. Be sure to include payment if there is a charge for the material. If no price is listed, the material is free. Films listed are available on a free loan basis.

Sample Letter

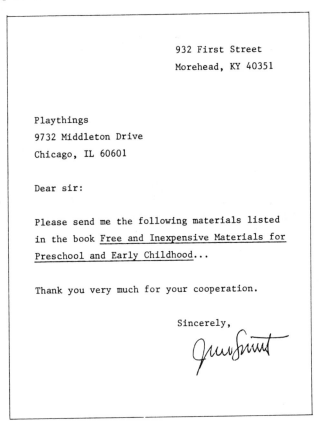

```
                                    932 First Street
                                    Morehead, KY 40351


        Playthings
        9732 Middleton Drive
        Chicago, IL 60601

        Dear sir:

        Please send me the following materials listed
        in the book Free and Inexpensive Materials for
        Preschool and Early Childhood...

        Thank you very much for your cooperation.

                                    Sincerely,
```

Animals and Pets

"Care of" Series

Pamphlets (9). Each describes the care of one of the following pets: birds, cats, dogs, fish, horses, ponies, burros, small animals, and wild animals and birds. American Humane Association, P.O. Box 1266, Denver, CO 80201.

The Children's Zoo*

Booklet. Includes the chimpanzee, mynah, gnu, armadillo, whale, penguin, seal, rhinoceros, camel, polar bear, and skunk. Free in classroom quantities to teachers of kindergarten through third grade only. Write on school letterhead. Eli Lilly and Company, Public Relations Services Dept., 307 East McCarty Street, Indianapolis, IN 46206.

The Farm*

Flannelboard packet. #30726. Helps children to understand farm animals, their uses, feed, and sounds, and how they are raised and protected. Thirty-two full-color pictures, record with six original songs, and six resource sheets. $3.75. David C. Cook Publishing Co., School Products Division, 850 North Grove Avenue, Elgin, IL 60120.

Good Kind Lion*

Leaflet: 4pp. Helps children relate to life around them by describing how a small animal might feel when they approach. Just as a child who meets a big lion would hope that the lion would do no harm, a bug or little animal, when approached by a child much larger than it, might hope the child was a "good kind lion." Single copy free. More than one copy, 3¢ each. KIND Youth Division, The National Humane Education Center, 2100 L Street NW, Washington, DC 20037.

Kindness Posters*

Posters (4). 14″ × 17″, full color. These posters illustrate the theme of kindness to animals. $1.00. American Humane Association, P.O. Box 1266, Denver, CO 80201.

Kittens and Cats*

Kit: booklets, posters, and bookmarks. Describes humane treatment and care of kittens and cats. Kit comes in two forms: kindergarten-third grade and fourth-sixth grades. One kit per teacher. Individual items from the kit may be ordered in classroom quantities. Write on school letterhead and state grade and number of students. American Humane Association, P.O. Box 1266, Denver, CO 80201.

Pet Birds*

Kit: booklets, posters, and bookmarks. Describes humane treatment and care of pet birds. Kit comes in two forms: kindergarten-third grade and fourth-sixth grades. One kit per teacher. Individual items from the kit may be ordered in classroom quantities. Write on school letterhead and state grade and number of students. American Humane Association, P.O. Box 1266, Denver, CO 80201.

Pets*

Set. #41467. Pictures of a variety of pets, emphasizing loving care, companionship, training, sanitation, medical attention, and handling. Twelve pictures in full color, with individual resource sheets that provide background objectives, questions, facts, stories, classroom activities, and lists of other resources. $3.75. David C. Cook Publishing Co., School Products Division, 850 North Grove Avenue, Elgin, IL 60120.

Puppies and Dogs*

Kit: booklets, posters, and bookmarks. Describes humane treatment and care of puppies and dogs. Kit comes in two forms: kindergarten to third grade and fourth to sixth grades. One kit per teacher. Individual items from the kit may be ordered in classroom quantities. Write on school letterhead and state grade and number of students. American Humane Association, P.O. Box 1266, Denver, CO 80201.

Small Animals*

Kit: booklets, posters, and bookmarks. Describes humane treatment and care of small animals. Kit comes in two forms:

kindergarten to third grade and fourth to sixth grades. One kit per teacher. Individual items from the kit may be ordered in classroom quantities. Write on school letterhead and state grade and number of students. American Humane Association, P.O. Box 1266, Denver, CO 80201.

A Trip to the Zoo*
Set. #24265. Involves children in learning about familiar and unfamiliar animals to appreciate similarities, differences, and beauty. Teaches origins, habits, and foods of the animals. The set consists of twelve animal pictures in color and twelve resource sheets giving background, facts, stories, questions, activities, and objectives. $3.75. David C. Cook Publishing Co., School Products Division, 850 North Grove Avenue, Elgin, IL 60120.

We All Like Milk*
Prints (12), 2pp. introductory sheet. #B002. This portfolio consists of twelve full-color pictures of mammals. Teacher's guide is on the back of each print. $2.00. The Food, Nutrition and Dairy Council, Shadyside Centre, 5100 Centre Avenue, Pittsburgh, PA 15232.

Art

Art Guide: Let's Create a Form
Bulletin: 64pp, full color. Professional help for teachers who want to guide and encourage children to express themselves through art. Developed by the San Diego County Department of Education. 1969. $2.50. Association for Childhood Education International, 3615 Wisconsin Avenue N.W., Washington, DC 20016.

Art Guide: Let's Make a Picture

Bulletin: 76pp, full color. Includes discussion of what one sees in a picture, as well as many specific teaching ideas from tempera painting to toothpick pictures. Developed by the San Diego County Department of Education. 1969. $2.25. Association for Childhood Education International, 3615 Wisconsin Avenue N.W., Washington, DC 20016.

Art Information Sheets

Brochure: 11pp. Description of various art materials and suggestions for their use. Available with no charge to art teachers. Milton Bradley Company, Springfield, MA 01101.

Art Magic

Booklet: 48pp. #373. More than 100 art projects—gifts, decorations, costumes, jewelry, holiday items—correlated with curriculum. $1.95. The Instructor Publications, Inc., Dansville, NY 14437.

Art Recipes

Booklet: 48pp. #330. Easy directions for making materials used in modeling, painting, etc.: finger paints, paste, inks, and so on. $1.95. The Instructor Publications, Inc., Dansville, NY 14437.

Avocado Pit-Nik Fact Sheets

Turn an avocado seed into "Magic Mouse," "Egbert Easter Bunny," "Humpty Dumpty," and other whimsical creatures. California Avocado Advisory Board News, 4533-B MacArthur Boulevard, Newport Beach, CA 92660.

Bulletin Board Ideas

Booklet: 48pp, illustrated. #332. Photographs of more than 150 bulletin boards will guide you in creating distinctive displays for every grade level and curriculum area. Explains simple lettering, 3-D effects, and projects with paper and scrap materials. $1.95. The Instructor Publications, Inc., Dansville, NY 14437.

Bulletin Boards for the Classroom
Booklet: 48pp. #351. A collection of bulletin board ideas with tips on topic selection, materials, display, lettering, and color choices. $1.95. The Instructor Publications, Inc., Dansville, NY 14437.

A Child's Right to the Expressive Arts
Booklet: 12pp. A position paper by Arne J. Nixon. Encourages development of environments that allow creativity to flourish; summarizes a child's rights. 1969. 15¢. Association for Childhood Education International, 3615 Wisconsin Avenue N.W., Washington, DC 20016.

Classroom Papercraft Projects and Patterns
Book: 56pp. #ISBN-0-8224-1415-5. By Margaret Goblirsch and Katherine M. Daly. Gives simple patterns and ideas that can be used for papercraft projects in the primary classroom. $2.50. Fearon Publishers, Inc., 6 Davis Drive, Belmont, CA 94002.

Clay Modeling Methods
Brochure: 2pp. #38. Discusses and illustrates various modeling methods, such as push and pull, pinch pot, coil, and slab. Single copy free to teachers. American Art Clay Company, 4717 West Sixteenth Street, Indianapolis, IN 46222.

Coloring Fun with Draw-A-Lot
Pamphlet. Gives many creative ideas for using Draw-A-Lot magic markers. Educational Material Dept., Carter's Ink Company, Cambridge, MA 02142.

Creative Arts and Crafts
Booklet: 44pp, illustrated. #3024. Carefully selected arts and crafts activities that can be done at home or at school. General activities for grades one through six. $1.95. Instructional Fair, Inc., 4158 Lake Michigan Drive, Grand Rapids, MI 49504.

Cut Yourself a Bunch of Fun

Booklet: 20pp, illustrated. Gives complete directions and patterns for making large decorative flowers. Includes a section of hints and skills. 25¢. Dennison Manufacturing Company, Framingham, MA 01701.

Easy-to-Makes

Booklet: 48pp. #359. Lists 100 art activities using everyday materials such as construction paper, paper plates, boxes, milk cartons, and scrap materials. Shows how to introduce a group project but still allow children to individualize their work. Organized around the months of the school year. $1.95. The Instructor Publications, Inc., Dansville, NY 14437.

Elementary Art Activities

Booklet: 32pp. #ISBN-0-8224-2675-7. By Barbara Bucher Linse. Gives a wide variety of art activities appropriate for elementary school children. $1.75. Fearon Publishers, Inc., 6 Davis Drive, Belmont, CA 94002.

Helping Children Draw

Booklet: 48pp. #353. Shows how to draw arms, legs, feet, hands, people, buildings, cartoons, and so on. $1.95. The Instructor Publications, Inc., Dansville, NY 14437.

Letter-Perfect Bulletin Boards

Booklet: 48pp. #364. Alphabet stencils, colors, and more. $1.95. The Instructor Publications, Inc., Dansville, NY 14437.

Lettering with a Felt Tip Marker

Pamphlet: 8pp. Gives examples of lettering and tips on poster making with markers. Educational Material Dept., Carter's Ink Company, Cambridge, MA 02142.

Making Dioramas and Displays

Book. #345. Contains information for making dioramas, developing displays, and making scenes of all kinds. Shows how to form animal and human figures, simulate various ground areas, and construct buildings. Discusses displays and racks. $1.95. The Instructor Publications, Inc., Dansville, NY 14437.

The Montessori Approach to Art Education
Booklet. #047-7. Discusses the "learning-by-doing" Montessori approach to art. Aimed especially toward the exceptional child's needs, but appropriate for all children. $1.95. Special Child Publications Division, Bernie Straub Publishing Co., 4535 Union Bay Place N.E., Seattle, WA 98105.

More Paper-Bag Puppets
Book: 64pp. #ISBN-0-8224-4520-4. By DeAtna M. Williams. Gives patterns with written directions for making paper-bag puppets. $2.50. Fearon Publishers, Inc., 6 Davis Drive, Belmont, CA 94002.

More Recipes for Fun
Book. Gives a wide range of activities for both early learners and older children. $2.50. PAR Project—Dept. PT, 464 Central Avenue, Northfield, IL 60093.

Paper Art
Booklet: 48pp. #331. Sixty-nine art ideas using all types of paper. Ideas for applying paint, crayon, chalk, and ink. $1.95. The Instructor Publications, Inc., Dansville, NY 14437.

Paper Arts and Crafts
for Teachers and Group Leaders
Booklet: 40pp. #00-556. Designed especially to aid the elementary school teacher with arts and crafts, bulletin boards, posters, costumes, and other visual learning. 50¢. Dennison Manufacturing Co., Dept. 53, Framingham, MA 01701.

Paper-Bag Puppets
Book: 64pp. #ISBN-0-8224-5275-8. By DeAtna M. Williams. Patterns with directions for making puppets appropriate for the

primary grades. $2.50. Fearon Publishers, Inc., 6 Davis Drive, Belmont, CA 94002.

Projects and Patterns
Book: 64pp. #01867. This book offers dozens of ideas and patterns based on things familiar to children. Patterns can be traced onto any kind of paper, then clipped out. Children can then color them for murals, collages, decorations, and handwork projects. $2.50. David C. Cook Publishing Co., School Products Division, 850 North Grove Avenue, Elgin, IL 60120.

Puppets for All Grades
Booklet: 48pp. #334. Sack, sock, stick, mache, ball, and personality puppets; ideas for all curriculum areas. $1.95. The Instructor Publications, Inc., Dansville, NY 14437.

Recipes for Busy Little Hands
Booklet: 46pp, illustrated. #43. By Doreen Croft. A great help to those who work with young children. Gives recipes for play dough, easel paints, finger paints, colored sand, modeling goop, soap snow, and fun-to-eat foods. $2.25. Day Care and Child Development Council of America, 1012 Fourteenth Street N.W., Washington, DC 20005.

Successful Bulletin Boards
Booklet: 48pp. #362. Nearly 125 ideas for holiday/special event displays; mounting; lettering; and so on. $1.95. The Instructor Publications, Inc., Dansville, NY 14437.

Suggestions for Your Art Education Program
Folder. Includes leaflets: "Crayola Crayons Art Techniques"; "Artista Water Colors Art Techniques"; "Crayola Modeling Clay Art Techniques"; Artista Art Chalks Art Techniques"; "Finger Paint Art Techniques"; and more. Binney and Smith, Inc., 380 Madison Avenue, New York, NY 10017.

Take a Handful of Letters
Book. Shows how to use purchased or homemade printing sets in imaginative ways to reinforce language arts, art, and other curriculum areas. The book is intended for children to use alone or for teachers to use as a resource for classroom activities. $2.00. Education Development Basis, 39 Chapel Street, Newton, MA 02160.

Your Art Idea Book
Book. #343. Describes more than 300 art projects. Gives quick ideas and aids for long-range planning. Discusses two- and three-dimensional projects, design, ways of printing, and types of construction. $1.95. The Instructor Publications, Inc., Dansville, NY 14437.

Audiovisual

Baths and Babies
Film: 18min., color. In step-by-step sequence, a professional nurse presents proper methods of bathing a baby. She shows how to prepare for bathing and how to hold the baby securely and confidently. She answers such questions as "When can I start bathing my baby?" and "What do I do if my baby cries?" Free loan: user pays return postage only. Association Films, Inc. (For ordering information see p. 16.)

Blueprint for Life
Film: 14min., color. Concerned parents of a child born with a birth defect visit a geneticist to learn what the risks are of having a second child born with a defect. Using animation and photomicrographs, the geneticist explains the nature of chromosomes, meiosis, mitosis, and fertilization. Free loan. The National Foundation, March of Dimes, P.O. Box 2000, White Plains, NY 10602.

The Case against Rubella

Film: 8min., color. Discusses and illustrates the tragic effects of rubella on a baby whose mother contracts it during pregnancy and the development and successful use of a vaccine to prevent rubella. Free loan. The National Foundation, March of Dimes, P.O. Box 2000, White Plains, NY 10602.

Copycat Puppet*

Puppet. #7001. This high-quality cloth Copycat puppet can be used for motivating Instructional Fair animated texts. Washable acrylic. $2.95. Instructional Fair, Inc., 4158 Lake Michigan Drive, Grand Rapids, MI 49504.

The Day the Bicycles Disappeared*

Film: 14min., color or b/w. Synopsis: When all the bicycles in town suddenly disappear, it turns out that they have met to protest the hazardous riding habits of their owners. Not until each rider signs a safe bicycling pledge do they agree to be taken home. 1967. Free loan. AAA Foundation for Traffic Safety, 734 Fifteenth Street N. W., Washington, DC 20005.

Diagnosis before Birth

Film: 8min., color. Presents scientific information on the roles of heredity and environment in fetal development. Explains prenatal and postnatal diagnosis of birth defects and various genetic counseling techniques. Free loan. The National Foundation, March of Dimes, P.O. Box 2000, White Plains, NY 10602.

First Two Weeks of Life

Film: 17min., color. A fascinating day-by-day visual "diary" of a natural childbirth. A useful film for young parents anticipating the birth of their first child. Free loan: user pays return postage only. Association Films, Inc. (For ordering information see p. 16.)

If These Were Your Children

Film: Part I, 28min.; Part II, 22min. A film in two parts for guidance counselors, school administrators, psychologists, and others professionally interested in the emotional welfare of young children. Part I depicts the activities and behavior of a group of second-grade children with their teachers during an ordinary school day. Part II is a panel discussion by child care experts about the children's behavior, with flashbacks of significant scenes from Part I. The films are planned to stimulate discussions on the importance of recognizing early signs of emotional difficulties. Free loan: user pays return postage only. Metropolitan Life Insurance Company, Health and Welfare Division, 1 Madison Avenue, New York, NY 10010.

Jamie

Film: 7min., color. A day in the life of Jamie Weaver, Poster Child for 1975. Jamie was born without eyes, but her enthusiasm, talent, and sense of humor make this film unforgettable. Free loan. The National Foundation, March of Dimes, P.O. Box 2000, White Plains, NY 10602.

Kids and Cookies*

Film: 14min., color. Winner of many major awards, this film presents every kid's dream of a trip through a cookie factory. It is narrated by the kids themselves as they wonder at row on row of cookies jogging along conveyors. One of the few films ever made entirely from a child's viewpoint, it is as educational as it is charming. Free loan: user pays return postage only. Association Films, Inc. (For ordering information see p. 16.)

Little Marty

Film: 5min., color. Highlights in a day with Marty, age 8, who was born with no arms and a short leg. With artificial arms and a built-up shoe, he feeds himself, paints, types, swims, and plays ball, revealing great determination and courage. Free loan. The National Foundation, March of Dimes, P.O. Box 2000, White Plains, NY 10602.

A Little Slow

Film: 14min., color. Tells the story of Billy and Carol, mildly mentally retarded young people, and the denials of ordinary legal rights they encounter at various stages of life. Free loan:

user pays return postage only. Association Films, Inc. (For ordering information see p. 16.)

Looking at Children

Film: 24min., color. Portrays early signs of health problems and conditions in children as seen by observant teachers. This film is useful in preparation and in-service training of teachers, school nurses, and others dealing with children, as well as for parent meetings and study groups. Free loan. Health and Welfare Division, Metropolitan Life Insurance Company, 1 Madison Avenue, New York, NY 10010.

Mr. Peanut's Guide to Nutrition*

Film: 32 or 29½min., color. This film is available in two forms. The first is a set of five separate, complete short films (#C793; 32min. running time), suited for a one-a-day projection. The second is an all-in-one version (#C288; 29½min.), appropriate if projection facilities are limited. Mr. Peanut leads the viewer through the ABCs of vitamins, protein, carbohydrates, fats, and minerals. An excellent two-page teacher's guide accompanies both versions. School requests also receive thirty booklets of "Mr. Peanut's Guide to Nutrition." Available only to elementary schools in Arizona, California, Connecticut, Florida, Illinois, Indiana, Maryland, Massachusetts, Michigan, New Jersey, New York, Ohio, Oregon, Pennsylvania, Rhode Island, Texas, Washington, and Wisconsin. Free loan: user pays return postage only. Association Films, Inc. (For ordering information see p. 16.)

Of Peanuts, Protein, and Pachyderms*

Film: 13½min., color. #J-652. Film tells the story of a grandfather and grandson having fun at the zoo and with home movies, while learning about food value. Free loan: user pays return postage only. Association Films, Inc. (For ordering information see p. 16.)

The Only Kid on the Block

Film: 15min., color and b/w. Dramatic story of the impact of a serious birth defect on a boy, his family, and neighbors, as told by his parents. Free loan. The National Foundation, March of Dimes, P.O. Box 2000, White Plains, NY 10602.

Otto the Auto*

Films: animated, 4½min. color films, available individually or in sets. Series A (1957): "Don't Cross between Parked Cars"; "Two Sleeping Lions"; "Cross at the Corner"; "The Little White Line That Cried"; "Wear White at Night"; "Inky and Blinky." Series B (1958): "Obey Your Safety Patrol"; "Otto Asks a Riddle"; "Look All Ways before Crossing"; "Otto Meets a Puppet"; "Be Extra Alert on Raining Days"; "The Bright Yellow Raincoat." Series C (1959):"Play Away from Traffic"; "Squeaky and His Playmates"; "Billy's New Tricycle"; "Walk on the Left Facing Traffic"; "Peter the Pigeon"; "Watch for Turning Cars"; " Timothy the Turtle." Series D (1971): "Does the Green Light Always Mean Go?"; "A Surprise for Otto"; "Otto Goes Ice Skating"; "Horseplay"; "The Secret of Pushbuttons." Free loan. AAA Foundation for Traffic Safety, 734 Fifteenth Street N.W., Washington, DC 20005.

Paula

Film: 7min., color. The private life of a poster child. Little Paula Pfeifer is shown at home, in school, playing with her brother and father, and visiting the zoo. Free loan. The National Foundation, March of Dimes, P.O. Box 2000, White Plains, NY 10602.

Ralph*

Hand puppet. Sunkist dinosaur. $1.00. Consumer Services, Sunkist Growers, Inc., P.O. Box 7888, Van Nuys, CA 91409.

The Safest Way*

Film: 14½min., color or b/w. Synopsis: As a parent-child-teacher project, each pupil maps out the safest route from his home to school. 1962. Free loan. AAA Foundation for Traffic Safety, 734 Fifteenth Street N.W., Washington, DC 20005.

The Talking Car*
Film: 16½min., color. Synopsis: After nearly being hit when he runs into the street without first looking for oncoming cars, Jimmy—in a dream sequence—is grilled by a tribunal of three talking cars. He must show how well he knows the "see and be seen" traffic safety rules. 1969. Free loan. AAA Foundation for Traffic Safety, 734 Fifteenth Street N.W., Washington, DC 20005.

The Time of Growing
Film: 29min. #MLS-604. This film is designed for parents, teachers, and others interested in the growth and development of children. It takes viewers to a second-grade classroom where candid observations are made of the youngsters in their daily activities. Free loan: user pays return postage only. Metropolitan Life Insurance Company, Health and Welfare Division, 1 Madison Avenue, New York, NY 10010.

Uncle Jim's Dairy Farm*
Film: 12min., color. #5-294. (For corresponding booklet, see "Food and Recipes" section.) This revised version of the perennial classroom favorite features wholesome daily living on a dairy farm, as seen through the eyes of two city-bred children. Designed to help mold ideals of healthy, happy living, the film emphasizes growth as a result of good nutrition. Free loan: user pays return postage only. Association Films, Inc. (For ordering information see p. 16.)

Wholly Cow*
Film: 10½min., color. #K-798. Did you ever wonder how a cow gives milk? This film tells the fascinating story of nature's own milk factory, the cow. It tells how, through a series of complicated yet easy-to-understand processes, the average milk cow gives about 100 pints of milk a day. Free loan: user pays return postage only. Association Films, Inc. (For ordering information see p. 16.)

Film Exchanges—Association Films

600 Grand Avenue, Ridgefield, NJ 07657. (201) 943-8200
512 Burlington Avenue, La Grange, IL 60525. (312) 352-3377
324 Delaware Avenue, Oakmont, PA 15139. (412) 828-5900
6644 Sierra Lane, Dublin, CA 94566. (415) 829-2300
7838 San Fernando Road, Sun Valley, CA 91352. (213) 767-7400
8615 Director's Row, Dallas, TX 75247. (214) 638-6791
410 Great Road, Littleton, MA 01460. (617) 486-3518
915 N. W. Nineteenth Avenue, Portland, OR 97209.
   (503) 226-7695
5797 New Peachtree Road, Atlanta, GA 30340. (404) 458-6251
6420 West Lake Street, Minneapolis, MN 55426. (612) 920-2095
333 Adelaide Street West, Toronto 133, Ontario, Canada.
   (416) EM 2-2501

Career Education

Doctor*

Show-and-tell book: 16pp. #36608. The doctor is shown on the
inside front cover. As pages are turned, full-color scenes with
children align with the cover illustration to show how youngsters
are assisted by a community helper and friend. $2.50. David C.
Cook Publishing Co., School Products Division, 850 North
Grove Avenue, Elgin, IL 60120.

Fireman*

Show-and-tell book: 16pp. #36590. The fireman is shown on the
inside front cover. As pages are turned, full-color scenes with
children align with the cover illustration to show how youngsters
are assisted by a community helper and friend. $2.50. David C.
Cook Publishing Co., School Products Division, 850 North
Grove Avenue, Elgin, IL 60120.

Policeman*

Show-and-tell book: 16pp. #36616. The policeman is shown on the inside front cover. As pages are turned, full-color scenes with children align with the cover illustration to show how youngsters are assisted by a community helper and friend. $2.50. David C. Cook Publishing Co., School Products Division, 850 North Grove Avenue, Elgin, IL 60120.

World of Work Unit*

Package. Includes an 85-frame filmstrip, complete with cassette, entitled "The World of Work as It Relates to the Citrus Industry." Also contains accompanying 8-page unit and game on the citrus industry, "To Market, to Market." $5.00. Consumer Services, Sunkist Growers, Inc., P.O. Box 7888, Van Nuys, CA 91409.

Yellow Pages of Learning Resources

Book: 94pp, illustrated. #78. Richard Saul Wurman, editor. Imitates telephone yellow pages to guide teachers in using community resources to provide learning opportunities. Includes what you can learn from department store, garbage man, gas station, and so on. $1.95. Day Care and Child Development Council of America, 1012 Fourteenth Street N.W., Washington, DC 20005.

Child Care and Development

(See also Audiovisual)

The ABC's of Perfect Posture

Booklet: 12pp. #OP-320. Tells what constitutes good posture and how to determine whether your posture is good. Presents a series of exercises for correcting posture problems. 25¢. American Medical Association, Health Education Materials, 535 Dearborn Street, Chicago, IL 60610.

As Your Child Grows—The First Eighteen Months

Booklet: 27pp. Based on a series of lectures on child study delivered by Katherine M. Wolf, a noted psychologist. Designed to help parents, especially new mothers, know what to expect of themselves and their infants during the first eighteen months of life. Offers both practical suggestions and psychological insights. $1.50 plus 50¢ for postage and service. Child Study Press, 50 Madison Avenue, New York, NY 10010.

Baby's Record Book

Booklet: 32pp. Brightly illustrated booklet for new parents. Gives information on first-year infant care and development, with space for keeping records on baby's progress: growth, first accomplishments, first teeth, immunization dates, and health notes. Includes additional resources for further parent education. Health and Welfare Division, Metropolitan Life Insurance Company, 1 Madison Avenue, New York, NY 10010.

Child Care

Booklet: 38pp, illustrated. Contains information useful to potential parents, counselors, teachers, and playground aides. Directed especially toward babysitting. Camp Fire Girls, Inc., 1740 Broadway, New York, NY 10019.

A Complete Guide to Diapering

Reprint. #759. Good advice on how to keep a baby comfortable and free from skin irritations, as well as tips on saving time and steps. 20¢. *Baby Talk* Magazine, 66 East Thirty-fourth Street, New York, NY 10016.

Creativity

Booklet. #1003-5-1J. Describes patterns of development, manifestations of creativity, common blocks to creative development, and ways to stimulate creativity. 75¢. National Education Association Order Dept., The Academic Bldg, Saw Mill Road, West Haven, CT 06516.

Developmental Curriculum
Book: 85pp. #B-6. By Lucia Ann McSpadden. A helpful guide
to making a curriculum "in response to the present and future of
the children." Focuses on the process of curriculum building
based on constant interaction of all persons, continual gathering
of additional resources and approaches, and an ability to deal
with the challenge of change. Highly recommended; useful as a
training text. $2.25. National Easter Seal Society for Crippled
Children and Adults, 2023 West Ogden Avenue, Chicago, IL
60612.

The First Six Weeks
Booklet: 40pp. Care of mother and newborn up to six-week
checkups. Includes feeding, diapering, bathing, dressing, treat-
ing minor ailments, and when to call the doctor. 70¢. New
Readers Press, P.O. Box 131, Syracuse, NY 13210.

Early Identification and Intervention Programs
for Infants with Developmental Delay
and Their Families
Book: 204pp. #E-51. By Constance U. Battle. A summary and
directory of programs throughout the United States for infants
at risk from birth to age three. 1973. $2.00. National Easter Seal
Society for Crippled Children and Adults, 2023 West Ogden
Avenue, Chicago, IL 60612.

Enjoy Your Child—Ages 1, 2, and 3
Booklet. #141. By James L. Hymes. Sound, simple advice and
information on what parents and child study workers can expect
from growing children, and how they can best help those in the
one- to three-year-old group. 35¢. Public Affairs Committee,
Inc., 381 Park Avenue South, New York, NY 10016.

How I Grow*
Tag. #B080. This attractive tag is for recording the height and
weight of children. It can be used by the nurse or the classroom

teacher. 3¢. The Food, Nutrition, and Dairy Council, Shadyside Centre, 5100 Centre Avenue, Pittsburgh, PA 15232.

The Infants We Care For
Book: 108pp. #211. Laura L. Dittman, editor. Discusses the care and development of infants and toddlers: goals for infant and family, working with the family, toddlers and their parents, practical points in operating a center or a home-based program for infants, selection and training of staff, evaluation of programs, and directions for the future. 1973. $2.00. National Association for the Education of Young Children, 1834 Connecticut Avenue N.W., Washington, DC 20009.

Neighborhood House Child Care Services
Brochure. #20130. Gives an overview of the operation of neighborhood house child care services in Seattle, Washington. 40¢. U.S. Government Printing Office, Public Documents Dept., Washington, DC 20402.

Perspectives on Child Care
Book: 64pp. #208. Eric E. Van Loon, editor. Gives perspective to national debate on the need for a major investment of federal funds in child care. Includes the magnitude of need, estimated costs, legislative concerns, and ethnic perspectives. 1973. $1.25. National Association for the Education of Young Children, 1834 Connecticut Avenue N.W., Washington, DC 20009.

Screening and Assessment
of Young Children at Developmental Risk
Monograph: 188pp. DHEW Publication #OS 73-90. Documents current thinking about early screening and assessment of young children who either have various developmental disabilities already or are at considerable risk of having them later. 1973. $2.40. U.S. Government Printing Office, Public Documents Dept., Washington, DC 20402.

Some Special Problems of Children
Aged Two to Five Years

Book: 61pp. By Nina Ridenour and Isabel Johnson. A classic in parent and child literature. A useful tool for pediatricians, public health nurses, social workers, nursery school teachers, home economics extension agents, clergymen, and others. 1966. $1.50 plus 50¢ for postage and service. Child Study Press, 50 Madison Avenue, New York, NY 10010.

Stimulation Activities Guide for Children
from Birth to 5 Years

Booklet. By Marilyn Krajicek. Offers simple, inexpensive activities which the mother can use to teach her child. Keyed to age levels. 1973. $1.50. Instructional Technology C-234, John F. Kennedy Child Development Center, University of Colorado Medical Center, 4200 East Ninth Avenue, Denver, CO 80220.

Successful Toilet Training

Reprint. #751. By T. Berry Brazelton. A simple toilet training program based on correct timing, which will help parents greatly. 20¢. *Baby Talk* Magazine, 66 East Thirty-fourth Street, New York, NY 10016.

Ways to Help Babies Grow and Learn

Book. By Leslie Segner, Ph.D. This partial infant curriculum is an integral part of an entire preschool curriculum being developed at the John F. Kennedy Center. It contains guidelines for infant educators; language development guidelines to help the child learn to understand what is said and to communicate thoughts he is thinking; personal-social development guidelines to help the child learn self-care, social skills, and self-esteem; fine-motor development guidelines to help the child learn the use of eyes and hands; gross-motor development guidelines to help the child learn to crawl, walk, jump, climb, and skip; and an appendix with information on commercially available toys, toys that can be made, nursery rhymes and singing games, and the importance of music for babies and toddlers. $3.70. Instructional Technology C-234, John F. Kennedy Child Development Center, University of Colorado Medical Center, 4200 East Ninth Avenue, Denver, CO 80220.

What to Expect of Baby
from One to Twelve Months

Booklet: 30pp. #701. A series of articles on baby's development throughout the first year. Illustrated with dramatic photographs, this booklet gives a great deal of useful advice on handling various problems at specific ages. 30¢. *Baby Talk* Magazine, 66 East Thirty-fourth Street, New York, NY 10016.

Your Baby's Eyes

Booklet: 8pp. Explains the development of vision in infants. Suggests ways to help children develop their vision correctly. Single copy free. Public Information Division, American Optometric Association, 7000 Chippewa Street, St. Louis, MO 63119.

Your Child from 1 to 6

Booklet. #413. Covers health and safety needs of the baby who has begun to walk. 20¢. Office of Child Development, U.S. Department of Health, Education, and Welfare, Superintendent of Document, U.S. Government Printing Office, Washington, DC 20402.

Citizenship and Community

Children and the Law*

Set. #29355. For learning respect for the rights and property of others; how laws are made for everyone's benefit, protection, and personal safety; and the value of honesty and cooperation.

Twelve colorful pictures and twelve resource sheets containing objectives, learning activities, suggestions, discussion facts, background, and stories. $3.75. David C. Cook Publishing Co., School Products Division, 850 North Grove Avenue, Elgin, IL 60120.

The Circus*
Flannelboard packet. #29397. To aid color recognition, comparisons, muscle development, and participation. Twenty-four flannelgraph pictures, record with six songs, and resource sheet. $3.75. David C. Cook Publishing Co., School Products Division, 850 North Grove Avenue, Elgin, IL 60120.

Helping and Sharing*
Flannelboard packet. #24208. Aids in teaching young children how they can be helpful, generous, and cooperative. Nineteen pictures, with record and resource sheets. $3.75. David C. Cook Publishing Co., School Products Division, 850 North Grove Avenue, Elgin, IL 60120.

My Community*
Flannelboard packet. #24216. Illustrated action songs familiarize children with helpers and their places in the community. Eighteen colorful flannelgraph pictures, record, and teacher resource sheets. $3.75. David C. Cook Publishing Co., School Products Division, 850 North Grove Avenue, Elgin, IL 60120.

My Community*
Set. #24232. Explains services provided and maintained by the community. An excellent social studies enrichment material for classwork and popular field trips. Set consists of twelve full-color pictures and individual resource sheets containing suggestions, ideas, learning activities, rhythmic activities, stories, background information, and listings of other resources. $3.75. David C. Cook Publishing Co., School Products Division, 850 North Grove Avenue, Elgin, IL 60120.

School and School Helpers*

Set. #44693. Developed to help young students understand that many people are needed to run their school. Guides them to appreciate the opportunity to learn and achieve. Students learn the important functions maintained to meet their needs. Twelve full-color pictures plus twelve resource sheets containing suggested aims, learning activities, discussion topics, rhythmic activities, ideas, and lists of other resources. $3.75. David C. Cook Publishing Co., School Products Division, 850 North Grove Avenue, Elgin, IL 60120.

Social Development*

Set. #24257. Encourages young students to recognize it is fun to share, communicate, play, sing, help, and cooperate with others. Helps develop essential social attitudes. Twelve full-color pictures and twelve resource sheets containing suggested aims, discussion questions, learning activities, rhythmic activities, stories, and other resources. $3.75. David C. Cook Publishing Co., School Products Division, 850 North Grove Avenue, Elgin, IL 60120.

This Is Our Flag*

Poster: 11″ × 15″. Picture of the U.S. flag with the legend, "Be Proud of It." For framing and display. 1970. 75¢. U.S. Government Printing Office, Public Documents Dept., Washington, DC 20402.

Dental Health

Casper and the Friendly Dentist*

Comic book: 16pp, color. #G30. For elementary school children. Casper the Friendly Ghost (a widely known children's comic book character) helps a dentist, Dr. Grin, show Mary and Mark around his office. Dr. Grin and Casper give the children advice about keeping their teeth healthy. $1.55 for 25 copies. Bureau of Dental Health Education, American Dental Association, 211 East Chicago Avenue, Chicago, IL 60611.

Casper and Space-Age Dentistry*
Comic book: 16pp. #647. Casper the Friendly Ghost takes some children on a tour of the Health Center at Cape Kennedy. A staff dentist tells the kids how to take care of their teeth and keep generally healthy, like the astronauts. $1.75 for 25 copies. Bureau of Dental Health Education, American Dental Association, 211 East Chicago Avenue, Chicago, IL 60611.

"D" is for Dentist*
Comic book: 16pp, color. #G44. In this story for preschoolers, Janie, a primary pupil, teaches and learns from her class of preschoolers about a child's first visit to the dentist. $1.55 for 25 copies. Bureau of Dental Health Education, American Dental Association, 211 East Chicago Avenue, Chicago, IL 60611.

Dental Care for the Handicapped
Leaflet: 6pp. #A-191. By Wesley O. Young. Discusses the special dental needs of the handicapped child and community programs to provide dental care. 1965. 10¢. National Easter Seal Society for Crippled Children and Adults, 2023 West Ogden Avenue, Chicago, IL 60612.

Do You?*
Poster: #P529. Miniature: #B044. Teacher's guide, 2pp. Focuses on the importance of regular toothbrushing, visits to the dentist, and proper foods for dental health. 25¢ per poster; 1¢ per miniature. Food, Nutrition, and Dairy Council, Shadyside Centre, 5100 Centre Avenue, Pittsburgh, PA 15232.

Dudley the Dragon*
Comic book: 16pp, color. #G45. Written in verse for preschool and primary children. Based on the American Dental Association film #DHTV-99. A village boy teaches Dudley, the local dragon, about good dental health. Dudley, in turn, shows the

villagers how to brush properly and is loved by all. $1.55 for 25 copies. Bureau of Dental Health Education, American Dental Association, 211 East Chicago Avenue, Chicago, IL 60611.

Elementary School Posters*

Posters(4): 3 " × 4 ", color. #S8 a–d. These small posters carry a dental health message for young patients. $1.25 for 25 copies. Bureau of Dental Health Education, American Dental Association, 211 East Chicago Avenue, Chicago, IL 60611.

Frayed Toothbrush Mini-Poster*

Poster: 3 " × 5 ". #S23. One side has a picture of a frayed toothbrush with the legend, "Splurge!" The reverse side tells how to select and care for toothbrushes. 35¢ for 25 copies. Bureau of Dental Health Education, American Dental Association, 211 East Chicago Avenue, Chicago, IL 60611.

I'm Going to the Dentist*

Booklet, two colors. #G1. A picture story with a brief text for parents to read to young children. Tells about a small boy's visit to the dentist. Includes a foreword for parents. $2.05 for 25 copies. Bureau of Dental Health Education, American Dental Association, 211 East Chicago Avenue, Chicago, IL 60611.

Learning about Your Oral Health

Brochure. Lists and describes various teaching aids and materials for instruction about oral health. Bureau of Dental Health Education, American Dental Association, 211 East Chicago Avenue, Chicago, IL 60611.

Pointers for Parents:
Your Child's First Visit to the Dentist

Booklet, illustrated. #G10. Advice for parents who are taking their children to the dentist for the first time. Produced with the cooperation of the American Society of Dentistry for Children. $2.55 for 100 copies. Bureau of Dental Health Education, American Dental Association, 211 East Chicago Avenue, Chicago, IL 60611.

A Preventive Care Guide
for Multihandicapped Children:
Dental Care Begins at Home

Leaflet: 2pp. #L-82. By Albert Green. Practical advice for parents. Also suggests where local dentists may obtain information. Single copy free; $10.00 for 150 copies. National Easter Seal Society for Crippled Children and Adults, 2023 Ogden Avenue, Chicago, IL 60612.

A Visit to the Dentist*

Booklet, illustrated in color. #S14. The brief text describes Judy and Johnny's visit to the dentist. When Judy returns to school, she tells the other children in her class about her experiences. $4.10 for 25 copies. Bureau of Dental Health Education, American Dental Association, 211 East Chicago Avenue, Chicago, IL 60611.

What Happened to Mike?*

Leaflet, two colors. # G34. Tells the story of a polar bear named Mike who lost a tooth because he was overly fond of sweets. Points out that a bear can't learn how to take care of his teeth, but a child can. Gives rules for good dental health. $2.20 for 100 copies. Bureau of Dental Health Education, American Dental Association, 211 East Chicago Avenue, Chicago, IL 60611.

Education

Animated Arithmetic*

Book: 52pp. #4039. Cartoon characters and unique problems motivate children into enrichment and basic activities in the new math. Designed for individualized sequential skill and concept development. The skills and concepts developed are listed with each activity. $1.95. Instructional Fair, Inc., 4158 Lake Michigan Drive, Grand Rapids, MI 49504.

Basic Number Skills and Concepts

Book 50pp. #5044. Sequences number concepts and skills, including counting to twenty and beginning subtraction. Examples of concepts are over-under, largest-smallest, and first-second-third. There are twenty skill tests in counting, two in measurement, four in correspondence, five in numeration, and two in addition and subtraction. Gives 200 creative activities to teach the fifty crucial concepts in the text. $3.95. Instructional Fair, Inc., 4158 Lake Michigan Drive, Grand Rapids, MI 49504.

Bilingual Early Childhood Program

Pamphlet. #OE 20134. A bilingual early childhood program in San Antonio, Texas, is discussed with a brief description. 30¢. U.S. Government Printing Office, Public Documents Dept., Washington, DC 20402.

Children of Resurrection City

Bulletin: 48pp. A thoughtful and moving look at poverty's children, viewed through the experiences of a teacher and psychiatrist. A stimulus for serious questioning. 1970. $1.50. Association for Childhood Education International, 3615 Wisconsin Avenue N.W., Washington, DC 20016.

A Child's Record Book

Booklet: 20pp. #5049. For recording the 200 or more skills and concepts grouped as Cognitive and Readiness Skills, Self Care and Body Usage Skills, and Basic Number Skills and Concepts. Included is a 7-page general information section much like a case study form. There is room for anecdotal record keeping. This text can function as a complete listing of objectives for early childhood education. $1.50. Instructional Fair, Inc., 4158 Lake Michigan Drive, Grand Rapids, MI 49504.

Classroom Activity Cards

Cards. #312. How to make and use activity cards. More than 100 model cards, plus variations. Cards for all curriculum areas. $1.95. The Instructor Publications, Dansville, NY 14437.

Cognitive and Mental Development in the First Five Years of Life: A Review of Recent Research

Book: 111pp. #86. This National Institute for Mental Health report theorizes that young children live and develop best through productive "actions." Action orientation is explored in detail, and the report calls for "development of national understanding and commitment to the promotion of life for masses of children, rather than toleration for the turning off, the closing out of life for them at an early age." $2.00. Day Care and Child Development Council of America, 1012 Fourteenth St. N.W., Washington, DC 20005.

Color Book Craze

Leaflet: 8pp. By Blanche Jefferson. A critical look at coloring books, challenging false claims of their value and suggesting creative alternatives. 1964. 25¢ each. Association for Childhood Education International, 3615 Wisconsin Avenue N.W., Washington, DC 20016.

Creative Enrichment

Booklet: 48pp. #3021. Creative enrichment in language arts and social studies for grades one, two, and three, and in social studies and science for grades four, five, and six. Suggests teacher dialogue and hundreds of creative and critical thinking activities within open-ended themes. $1.95. Instructional Fair, Inc., 4158 Lake Michigan Drive, Grand Rapids, MI 49504.

Critical Incidents

Book: 52pp. #3025. Children are given a problem from school or home living; they must identify that problem and suggest appropriate solutions. Develops critical thinking ability and sympathetic responses and aids oral expression. Meets elementary social studies objectives with actual incidents placed on grade levels one through six. $1.95. Instructional Fair, Inc., 4158 Lake Michigan Drive, Grand Rapids, MI 49504.

Cross Cultural Family Center

Pamphlet. #OE20132. Discusses the Cross Cultural Family Center in San Francisco, California, and gives appropriate information about its operation. 35¢. U.S. Government Printing Office, Public Documents Dept., Washington, DC 20402.

Curriculum Is What Happens: Planning Is the Key

Book: 72pp. #119. Laura L. Dittmann, editor. A collection of original articles to help teachers in the critical area of curriculum planning. Specific means for facilitating self-directed learnings are emphasized. Emergent, prescribed, and accidental curricula are differentiated. 1970. $1.75. National Association for the Education of Young Children, 1834 Connecticut Avenue N.W., Washington, DC 20009.

Day Care for America's Children

Booklet. #470. By E. Robert La Crosse. Discusses current pressures for day care programs, what goes into these programs, and what needs to be done about them. 35¢. Public Affairs Committee, Inc., 381 Park Avenue South, New York, NY 10016.

Early Childhood Education

Booklet: 48pp. #375. Guiding the living-learning of child and group. Discusses settings for discovery, and so on. $1.95. The Instructor Publications, Inc., Dansville, NY 14437.

Early Learning Experiences

Book. #382. Explores seven areas of the curriculum: music, art, oral expression, literature, creative dramatics, numbers, and science. Discusses the philosophy of learning, guidelines for teaching, and classroom activities for early learners. $1.95. The Instructor Publications, Inc., Dansville, NY 14437.

Education for the Spanish Speaking

Book. By Ann Kelley. Reports on the development of bilingual programs and corresponding test instruments in Boston,

Massachusetts, and Washington, D.C. The author views the training of Spanish-speaking youngsters as a combination of academic skills and recognition of their heritage. The political difficulties involved in establishing bilingual education programs are also discussed. $1.75. Education Development Center, 39 Chapel Street, Newton, MA 02160.

Effective Learning and Teacher-Pupil Ratio

Leaflet: 4pp. This position paper by Alice V. Keliher calls for class size that allows individuality, humanity, and creativity to flourish. 1966. 10¢. Association for Childhood Education International, 3615 Wisconsin Avenue N.W., Washington, DC 20016.

English Primary Schools

Book: 100pp. # 134. By Elliot W. Eisner. Surveys the organization, curriculum, methods of evaluation, and students' and teachers' roles in English primary schools. Provides a basis for planning similar programs in American schools. 1974. $2.50. National Association for the Education of Young Children, 1834 Connecticut Avenue N.W., Washington, DC 20009.

Enhancing Developmental Progress in Preschool Exceptional Children

Book: 152pp. #ISBN-O-8224-5630-3. By Alton D. Quick, Thomas L. Little, and A. Ann Campbell. Helps educators establish early childhood remediation programs based on the nationally acclaimed model developed at Memphis State University. Explains the goals of the program and tells how to set up a similar program. 1974. List $4.00; school $3.00. Fearon Publishers, Inc., 6 Davis Drive, Belmont, CA 94002.

Evaluating Children's Progress: A Rating Scale for Children in Day Care

Book: 50pp, illustrated. #9X. Provides scales for rating development and learning, related to specific ages, for use with individual children and groups. The format of these rating scales is clear and easy to use. Instructions are included. $2.00. Day Care and Child Development Council of America, 1012 Fourteenth Street N.W., Washington, DC 20005.

The Expressive Arts for the Mentally Retarded

Book: 86pp. #30-5. Prepared by David R. Gingled. Articles on art, arts and crafts, communication and language, dance, dramatics, and music. $1.25. National Association for Retarded Citizens, P.O. Box 6109, Arlington, TX 76011.

For Handicapped Preschoolers—
Early Childhood Education

Booklet: 46pp. #99. Includes "The Children Who Had to Be Found," by W. E. Densham; "Bureau of Education for the Handicapped Commitment and Program in Early Childhood Education," by E. W. Martin; "Model Centers for Preschool Handicapped Children—Year II," by G. M. Olshin; "Early Detection and Remediation of Learning Disabilities," by B. Dubnoff; and "Additional Sources for Further Reading." $1.75. Day Care and Child Development Council of America, 1012 Fourteenth Street N.W., Washington, DC 20005.

"The Good Life" for Infants and Toddlers

Booklet: 48pp. #124. By Mary Elizabeth Keister. How do we provide high-quality care for infants in groups outside the home? This booklet describes a demonstration program of daytime care which examines the essential elements of the environment, staff, materials, and program. Includes a compilation of useful references. 1970. $1.50. National Association for the Education of Young Children, 1834 Connecticut Avenue N.W., Washington, DC 20009.

Guess What

Booklet: 40pp. #3023. Puzzles, games, activities, newspaper stories, and problems in the social studies and science to develop critical and abstract thinking ability. The problems can be read to or by children. $1.95. Instructional Fair, Inc., 4158 Lake Michigan Drive, Grand Rapids, MI 49504.

Guidelines for Testing Minority Group Children ✓

Pamphlet: 18pp. #R174. Explains the conditions which prevent disadvantaged children, most of whom are minority group members, from demonstrating their mental potentialities in school-administered I.Q. tests. 35¢. Anti-Defamation League of B'Nai B'Rith, 315 Lexington Avenue, New York, NY 10016.

Housing for Early Childhood Education

Book: 84pp. #29. Current ideas about the physical environment for early childhood education. Useful for those planning to construct or remodel a facility and for those equipping or arranging an area for children. $1.50. Day Care and Child Development Council of America, 1012 Fourteenth Street N.W., Washington, DC 20005.

I Saw a Purple Cow
and 100 Other Recipes for Learning

Book: 96pp, illustrated. #39. Contains recipes for learning, using homemade equipment to provide enjoyable and developmental experiences. Useful for parents. $2.95. Day Care and Child Development Council of America, Inc., 1012 Fourteenth Street N.W., Washington, DC 20005.

Ideas That Work with Young Children ✓

Book: 236pp. #304. Katherine Read Baker, Editor. This selection of thirty-seven articles from past issues of *Young Children* gives practical, valuable information for teachers who are developing programs for young children or looking for new ideas. The seven sections include: understanding children and teaching; setting up a learning environment; language experiences; parents and teachers; areas of special challenge; and consulting with people in other professions. 1973. $3.00. National Association for the Education of Young Children, 1834 Connecticut Avenue N.W., Washington DC 20009.

Introducing Children to Math ✓

Booklet: 48pp. #386. Ideas for more than 100 modern math activities, emphasizing quantity, numbers, counting money, addition, subtraction, and position. $1.95. The Instructor Publications, Inc., Dansville, NY 14437.

An Inventory of Primary Skills

Booklet: 16pp. #ISBN-0-8224-3950-6. An inventory form for use with kindergarten and transitional primary children. Contains 300 primary skills, including tasks covering such areas as self-information, body identification, body spatial relations, copying design, and alphabet and number printing. 1970. $1.00. Fearon Publishers, Inc., 6 Davis Drive, Belmont, CA 94002.

The Learning Calendar

Calendar. Six weeks of fun learning for children at home with parents. Skills emphasized are listening, speaking, reading, value learning, and comprehension. 90¢. Moreno Educational Co., 7050 Belle Glade Lane, San Diego, CA 92119.

Learning Centers: Children on Their Own

Bulletin: 84pp. Combines theory and practice. Describes models of individualized teaching. Discusses roles, organization, evaluation, helpful hardware, and open space. $2.50. Association for Childhood Education International, 3615 Wisconsin Avenue N.W., Washington, DC 20016.

Let's See*

Booklet: 28pp. Educational activity book for five- to seven-year-olds. Includes puzzles to solve, drawings to color, hidden shapes to find, lines to connect, and many other activities. Teaches awareness of vision care. Single copy 50¢. Public Information Division, American Optometric Association, 7000 Chippewa Street, St. Louis, MO 63119.

Living and Learning with Children

Book: 64pp. By Paula Jorde. A handbook of activities for parents of three- to six-year-old children. This book gives valuable learning experiences that are simple, inexpensive, and fun. Paula Jorde has compiled games, toys, and activities that parent and child can enjoy together. Areas of learning emphasis include sensory awareness, getting ready to read and write, learning math concepts, discovering through science, creating through art and music, and cooking. $2.95. Shields Publications, 325 Ninth Street, San Francisco, CA 94103.

Logical-Mathematical Thinking
and the Preschool Classroom

Booklet: 32pp, illustrated. #186. By Jeanne Walton. Introduces twelve activities to aid children in developing abilities to think logically and to use numbers. An introduction describes Piaget's contribution to preschool teaching and calls for use of creativity. 75¢. Day Care and Child Development Council of America, 1012 Fourteenth Street N.W., Washington, DC 20005.

Mini Units

Units. Titles include: A Balloon and Funnel Pump; Building Blocks from Milk Cartons; Exploring with Food Coloring; Making Simple Books; Organdy Screening; A Pie Plate Water Wheel; Siphon Bottles; A Spinning Top That Writes; Stained Glass Cookies; and A Tin Can Pump. 20¢ each; combination packet of 10 for $2.00 plus 50¢ postage and handling. Teacher Shop, Children's Museum, Jamaica Way, Boston, MA 02130.

Nursery School Bulletin Boards

Book: 64pp. #ISBN-O-8224-4786-X. By Clare Cherry. Gives ideas, pictures, and descriptions for constructing bulletin boards for preschool and early childhood programs. $2.50. Fearon Publishers, Inc., 6 Davis Drive, Belmont, CA 94002.

Planning Environments for Young Children:
Physical Space

Book: 56pp. #115. By Sybil Kritchersky and Elizabeth Prescott, with Lee Walling. Analyzes the significance of the physical environment. Shows how space and the arrangement of equipment can invite and facilitate participation or, conversely, inhibit participation and create tensions. Includes illustrations and a workable method to analyze a school's physical environment. 1969. $1.50. National Association for the Education of Young Children, 1834 Connecticut Avenue N.W., Washington, DC 20009.

Play as a Learning Medium

Book: 123pp. #306. Doris Sponseller, editor. Learning through play occurs in every domain of the young child's life. Topics include: theories and research on the value of play, effective management of play environments, play in Piaget's view of problem solving, and encouraging social-dramatic play. This book is filled with anecdotes showing how children learn through play. A valuable resource for developing a broader understanding of the value of play as a learning medium. 1974. $2.85. National Association for the Education of Young Children, 1834 Connecticut Avenue N.W., Washington, DC 20009.

A Pre-Primary Program

Book: 50pp. #5046. Sequenced lesson plans, including pretests, posttests, methods, and teacher dialogue, for prereading skill and concept development and beginning numeration skill (to ten). $1.95. Instructional Fair, Inc., 4158 Lake Michigan Drive, Grand Rapids, MI 49504.

Primary School Portfolio

Leaflets (12). These practical, helpful leaflets focus on children ages six to nine: curriculum, activities, discipline, and so on. 1968. $1.25. Association for Childhood Education International, 3615 Wisconsin Avenue N.W., Washington, DC 20016.

Project WEY

Booklet. Discusses a pilot school/community project in environmental education located near Berkeley, California. An excellent creative guide for developing environmental learning areas. $1.00. Department of Landscape Architecture, University of California, Berkeley, CA 94720.

Promoting Cognitive Growth:
A Developmental-Interaction Point of View

Book: 64pp. #126. By Barbara Biber, Edna Shapiro, and David Wickens, in collaboration with Elizabeth Gilkeson. A unique presentation of actual episodes and interactions, giving specific attention to the role of the teacher in facilitating cognitive learning. Includes an excellent statement of educational goals for the preschool years, reflecting the philosophy of Bank Street College of Education. 1971. $2.50. National Association for the Education of Young Children, 1834 Connecticut Avenue N.W., Washington, DC 20009.

The Scrap Book

Book: 140pp. Written by teachers and parents, this book contains a wide variety of activities suited for three-, four-, and five-year-olds in all kinds of home and school settings. 1972. $2.50. Payment must accompany order. Friends of Perry Nursery School, 1541 Washtenaw, Ann Arbor, MI 48104.

Seventy Activities for Classroom Learning Centers

Booklet: 48pp. #317. Criteria, organization, and management of learning centers. Activities for reading, written language, mathematics, science, and social studies. $1.95. The Instructor Publications, Inc., Dansville, NY 14437.

So You Are Teaching in the Kindergarten

Book: 53pp. Educational Service Publication #30. By Betty Ann Roth. Guidebook for student teachers. 1965. Single copy $2.00. Extension Service, University of Northern Iowa, Cedar Falls, IA 50613.

Sources of Free and Inexpensive Pictures

Booklet: 32pp. #CPS2. Lists all kinds of pictures, many of which are difficult to find. Colorful pictures are available free or at very nominal cost to build a picture file in a variety of subject areas. This is one of the most comprehensive and complete source booklets. 1973. $1.00. Bruce Miller Publications, P.O. Box 369, Riverside, CA 92502.

Sources of Free and Inexpensive Teaching Aids

Booklet: 32pp. #CPS1. This is the twenty-seventh edition of this well-known booklet, whose first edition was published in 1939. It lists hundreds of sources of educational materials, all approved and carefully annotated. For all grade levels including college, sources are listed in almost every field of interest. 1972. $1.00. Bruce Miller Publications, P.O. Box 369, Riverside, CA 92502.

Tacoma Public Schools Early Childhood Program

Brochure. #20160. The Tacoma Public Schools Early Childhood Program is explained, with a brief description of its operation. 35¢. U.S. Government Printing Office, Public Documents Dept., Washington, DC 20402.

Teaching Materials Catalog

Leaflet. Lists service publications, including article reprints, for teachers, students, and parents. Some materials are keyed to *World Book* or to *Childcraft—The How and Why Library.* Free. Field Enterprises Educational Corporation, Merchandise Mart Plaza, Chicago, IL 60654.

Through the Year with Childcraft

Book: 64pp. Activity book for preschool and primary grades with suggestions to fit the months and season. Keyed to learning units in *Childcraft—The How and Why Library.* $1.00. Field Enterprises Educational Corporation, Merchandise Mart Plaza, Chicago, IL 60654.

Environmental

Bulletin Boards for Environmental Studies

Booklet: 48pp. #320. Activities to use with twenty-nine easy-to-make displays about plants, animals, air, water, minerals/fuels, soil, and so on. $1.95. The Instructor Publications, Inc., Dansville, NY 14437.

Flannelboard Stories*
Four stories about snacking, nutrition, ecology, and the environment. $1.00. Consumer Services, Sunkist Growers, Inc., P.O. Box 7888, Van Nuys, CA 91409.

A Story for Young Americans—
You Can Be a Conservationist*
Booklet. A story about the young conservationist. A good source of ecology information. 25¢. The American Forestry Association, 1319 Eighteenth Street N.W., Washington, DC 20036.

Trees Every Boy and Girl Should Know*
Book. Full of information that can relate to conservation, ecology, or science studies. $3.00. American Forestry Association, 1319 Eighteenth Street N.W., Washington, DC 20036.

Exceptional Children

(See also Audiovisual)

ABC's for Parents
Leaflet: 3pp. #A-193. By Marybeth P. Frey. Aids to management of the slow child at home. 10¢. National Easter Seal Society for Crippled Children and Adults, 2023 West Ogden Avenue, Chicago, IL 60612.

Advertencias para los Padres de Ninos Sordos
y Medio-Sordos
Leaflet. #A-248. By Jean Litley Lehman. Spanish edition of "Do's and Don'ts for Parents of Pre-school Deaf and Hard of Hearing Children." 15¢. National Easter Seal Society for Crippled Children and Adults, 2023 West Ogden Avenue, Chicago, IL 60612.

Best Records and Books
for Exceptional and Handicapped Children
Catalog: 33pp. A unique source for phonograph records, books, and other enrichment materials for use by exceptional children and their parents or teachers. All materials have been carefully tested by experts working with children. Single copy free. Children's Music Center. 5373 West Pico Boulevard, Los Angeles, CA 90019.

Birth Defects: Questions and Answers
Leaflet. #9-0007. Key facts about the nature, causes, prevention, and treatment of birth defects. The National Foundation, March of Dimes, P.O. Box 2000, White Plains, NY 10602.

Birth Defects: The Tragedy and the Hope
Booklet: 4pp, illustrated. #9-0026. Provides a comprehensive overview of what birth defects are and what can be done about them. The National Foundation, March of Dimes, P.O. Box 2000, White Plains, NY 10602.

The Brain Injured Child
Leaflet: 20pp. #E-36. By Richard S. Lewis. Speaking from long experience as a science writer and parent, the author describes the perceptually handicapped child and the nature of that child's handicaps. 25¢. National Easter Seal Society for Crippled Children and Adults, 2023 West Ogden Avenue, Chicago, IL 60612.

The Brain Injured Child in the Classroom
Leaflet: 14pp. #E-34. By Newell C. Kephart. Identifies stages of growth and development of children and explains why the brain injured child requires more basic methods of teaching. 35¢. National Easter Seal Society for Crippled Children and Adults, 2023 West Ogden Avenue, Chicago, IL 60612.

Building an Estate for a Crippled Child
Booklet: 23pp. #E-24. By John D. Riordan. A guide to planning for the financial security of a severely disabled child. 1959. 25¢.

National Easter Seal Society for Crippled Children and Adults, 2023 West Ogden Avenue, Chicago, IL 60612.

The Child with Spina Bifida Cystica
Leaflet: 5pp. #A-195. By Midlos Sugar. Discusses the nature of the disability and methods of treatment. 1965. 10¢. National Easter Seal Society for Crippled Children and Adults, 2023 West Ogden Avenue, Chicago, IL 60612.

Children with Special Problems:
A Manual for Day Care
Booklet: 20pp. #99-A. Marilyn Dashe, editor. Good descriptions of general and specific problems, and direct methods of coping with and helping children who have delayed development, orthopedic and medical problems, or speech, hearing, and visual problems. Gives case histories of each handicap with general guidelines on the problems involved and coping mechanisms to be used. $1.50. Day Care and Child Development Council of America, 1012 Fourteenth Street N.W., Washington, DC 20005.

Chromosome 21 and Its Association
with Down's Syndrome
Leaflet. #9-0023. Pictorializes chromosome 21 and its association with Down's Syndrome (mongolism). Covers standard trisomy, translocation, mosaicism, and clinical aspects. The National Foundation, March of Dimes, P.O. Box 2000, White Plains, NY 10602.

Confidencial
Leaflet. #9-0025. Spanish version òf "Confidential." The National Foundation, March of Dimes, P.O. Box 2000, White Plains, NY 10602.

Confidential
Leaflet. #9-0024. Written for men. Emphasizes the importance of prenatal care. The National Foundation, March of Dimes, Box 2000, White Plains, NY 10602.

Cooley's Anemia and Birth Defects Prevention

Leaflet, illustrated. #9-0041. Discusses key facts about Cooley's anemia (thalassemia). The National Foundation, March of Dimes, P.O. Box 2000, White Plains, NY 10602.

Designing for the Mentally Handicapped

Leaflet: 3pp. #A-189. By Daniel C. Bryant. Describes architectural facilities and equipment adapted to the special needs of the trainable mentally retarded. 10¢. National Easter Seal Society for Crippled Children and Adults, 2023 West Ogden Avenue, Chicago, IL 60612.

Do's and Don'ts for Parents of Pre-School Deaf and Hard of Hearing Children

Leaflet. #A-217. By Jean Litley Lehman. 15¢. National Easter Seal Society for Crippled Children and Adults, 2023 West Ogden Avenue, Chicago, IL 60612.

Early Recognition and Intervention: Programs for Children with Special Needs

Pamphlet: 16pp, illustrated. #9-B. By Peter Hainsworth and Cynthia Gilles. A guide to planning early screening programs in public schools, but useful to preschool programs as well. Emphasizes the need to involve parents and to avoid labeling children. Describes the who, when, where, what, and why of early detection and its follow-up of effective help for children with special needs. $1.00. Day Care and Child Development Council of America, Inc., 1012 Fourteenth Street N.W., Washington, DC 20005.

Easter Seal Guide to Programming for the Developmentally Handicapped Pre-school Child

Book: 85pp. #CT-18. A manual developed to assist Easter Seal Societies in planning and operating comprehensive child development programs for preschool-aged children and their families. Describes programming based on behavioral objectives. $1.50. National Easter Seal Society for Crippled Children and Adults, 2023 Ogden Avenue, Chicago, IL 60612.

Facts on Mental Retardation

Pamphlet: 15pp. #10-4. Questions and answers concerning the broad subject of mental retardation. Covers such areas as causes, prevention, cost, and steps required to meet the needs of the mentally retarded. 20¢. National Association for Retarded Citizens, P.O. Box 6109, Arlington, TX 76011.

Feeding the Cerebral Palsied Child

Poster: 8½ " × 11½ ". #A-204. A reproduction of a larger poster used at the Walter D. Matheny School for Cerebral Palsied Children. Demonstrates child development through self-help activities of eating. Single copy free. National Easter Seal Society for Crippled Children and Adults, 2023 West Ogden Avenue, Chigago, IL 60612.

A Guide for Parents
of Children Receiving Special Education

Leaflet: 2pp. #L-76. By James W. Allegra. Provides some general suggestions in answer to questions parents often ask. Single copy free; $10.00 for 150 copies. National Easter Society for Crippled Children and Adults, 2023 West Ogden Avenue, Chicago, IL 60612.

A Helpful Guide in the Training
of a Mentally Retarded Child

Pamphlet: 32pp. #20-2. By Elsie Blanton. Authoritative collection of suggestions for care and training of retarded children. Classifies activities by mental age. 50¢. National Association for Retarded Citizens, P.O. Box 6109, Arlington, TX 76011.

Helping the Slow Learner

Booklet. #405. By Millard Bienvenu, Sr. About one of every six American children is a slow learner. Describes the characteristics, limitations, and potentials of the slow learner and offers specific pointers to parents, teachers, and other school personnel. 35¢. Public Affairs Committee, Inc., 381 Park Avenue South, New York, NY 10016.

Is Your Child Blind?

Pamphlet: 8pp. F214. This newly revised and redesigned pamphlet shows parents of blind children how these children develop and grow and how they can help the children achieve their maximum potential. 1970. Up to 50 copies free. Publications Division, American Foundation for the Blind, 15 West Sixteenth Street, New York, NY 10011.

Learning Disorders, Hyperkinesis, and the Use of Drugs in Children

Leaflet: 7pp. #A-229. By Leon Oettinger, Jr. A review of the recent controversy over the use of drugs with school children and an authoritative discussion of the value of the amphetamines and methypenidate in the total treatment of children with learning disorders. 10¢. National Easter Seal Society for Crippled Children and Adults, 2023 West Ogden Avenue, Chicago, IL 60612.

Learning Disorders— Psychoneurological Disturbances in Childhood

Leaflet: 7pp. #D-34. By Helmer R. Myklebust. Explains the need for establishing criteria for adequate diagnosis and educational management of children with minimal brain damage. 25¢. National Easter Seal Society for Crippled Children and Adults, 2023 West Ogden Avenue, Chicago, IL 60612.

Letter to the Parent of a Cerebral Palsied Child

Leaflet. #A-111. By Mary Huber. Suggestions for day-to-day home training to aid in development of speech. 10¢. National Easter Seal Society for Crippled Children and Adults, 2023 West Ogden Avenue, Chicago, IL 60612.

Living with the Retarded

Booklet: 16pp. For everyone who needs to know how to relate to the retarded. Emphasizes social awareness: the problems of parents and community acceptance of the retarded person. 28¢. New Readers Press, P.O. Box 131, Syracuse, NY 13210.

Make the Most of Your Baby

Booklet. #20-7. By Mrs. June Mather. This booklet was written from the author's own personal viewpoint as the mother of two mentally retarded children. It also reflects her more than twenty years' experience in the mental retardation field. Her thesis is that children learn from play. The booklet tells how parents can provide meaningful play experiences for mentally retarded infants by being aware of the sequential nature of early childhood development. Single copy free. National Association for Retarded Citizens, P.O. Box 6109, Arlington, TX 76011.

The Mentally Handicapped Child under Five

Pamphlet: 20pp. #10-1. By Gunnar Dybwad. A survey of the kinds of services and support needed to handle adequately the problems of the family with a young retarded child. 25¢. National Association for Retarded Citizens, P.O. Box 6109, Arlington, TX 76011.

New Directions for Parents
of Persons Who Are Retarded

Book: 64pp. #10-25. By Robert A. Perske. For parents of a retarded child who seek to face their situation and deal with it in a creative way. The book focuses on attitudes and on regular family interactions which include handicapped children. $1.95. National Association for Retarded Citizens, P.O. Box 6109, Arlington, TX 76011.

Night Time and Your Handicapped Child:

Pamphlet: 26pp. #20-8. An article, "Prevention and Handling of Sleep Problems," by Shirley Cohen, Ph.D., and Edith Levitt, Ed.D., with illustrations by Priscilla Jean, Ph.D., Special Education Development Center, City University of New York at Hunter College. 25¢. National Association for Retarded Citizens, P.O. Box 6109, Arlington, TX 76011.

On Becoming a Parent of a Handicapped Child

Booklet: 18pp. #E-29. By Benjamin Spock. A discussion of the problems parents face in deciding what they can do to help their handicapped child and whom they may turn to for advice. 35¢. National Easter Seal Society for Crippled Children and Adults, 2023 West Ogden Avenue, Chicago, IL 60612.

Outline for Remediation of Problem Areas for Children with Learning Disabilities

Booklet: 13pp. #B-41. By Joan L. Bornstein. In outline form, presents some common problems, the identifiable behavior, and suggestions for amelioration. Prepared for distribution at the conference on "Teaching Methods for Children with Learning Disabilities," at the annual convention of the National Easter Seal Society, 1972. 25¢. National Easter Seal Society for Crippled Children and Adults, 2023 West Ogden Avenue, Chicago, IL 60612.

The Preschool Deaf-Blind Child, Suggestions for Parents.

Pamphlet: 8pp. F218. Gives suggestions to parents for helping deaf-blind children learn to walk, eat, dress themselves, and accomplish other details of everyday living. 1965. Up to 50 copies free. Publications Division, American Foundation for the Blind, 15 West Sixteenth Street, New York, NY 10011.

Responding to Individual Needs in Head Start

Book: 93pp, illustrated. HE 1.468: In 2/pt.1 S/N 1792-00016. Designed for Head Start staff, but equally valuable for parents and others involved in child care. Gives advice for teachers who work with children having physical, cognitive, or emotional problems. Suggests ways teachers can assist special children in group situations in which the special child may be meeting non-handicapped children for one of the first times. Describes activities in which blind, mentally retarded, hyperactive, and other special children can participate. Also includes medical information about childhood handicaps and health impairments. 1974. $1.85. U.S. Government Printing Office, Public Documents Dept., Washington, DC 20402.

The Responsibility of the Physician, Parent, and Child in Learning Disabilities

Leaflet: 6pp. #A-246. By Eric Denhoff. Suggestions to help physicians blend the art with the science of medicine to effectively meet the needs of children with learning disabilities and their families. 1974. 15¢. National Easter Seal Society for Crippled Children and Adults, 2023 West Ogden Avenue, Chicago, IL 60612.

Selected Reading Suggestions for Parents of Mentally Retarded Children

Pamphlet: 26pp. #10-15. List of available recent books and pamphlets from various sources covering areas of most interest to parents of mentally retarded children. Good basic bibliography. 40¢. National Association for Retarded Citizens, P.O. Box 6109, Arlington, TX 76011.

Self-Help Clothing for Handicapped Children

Book: 78pp, illustrated. #E-32. By Clari Bare. A guide for parents and professionals on how to design and adapt clothing that is easy to put on and take off. Contains a special section on teaching dressing skills. 75¢. National Easter Seal Society for Crippled Children and Adults, 2023 West Ogden Avenue, Chicago, IL 60612.

Tay-Sachs Disease and Birth Defects Prevention

Leaflet, illustrated. #9-0100. In questions and answers, explains this hereditary disease and the activities of the National Foundation in research and education. The National Foundation, March of Dimes, P.O. Box 2000, White Plains, NY 10602.

This Is Stevie's Story

Book: 192pp. #10-16. By Mrs Dorothy Murray, with an introduction by Pearl Buck. A mother's story of her mentally retarded son. Tells how Stevie's life was improved by the compassion and determination of his family when almost no other resources were available. $2.25. National Association for Retarded Citizens, P.O. Box 6109, Arlington, TX 76011.

Toilet Habits,
Suggestions for Training a Blind Child ✓
Pamphlet: 8pp. #F220. By Pauline M. Moor. Revised edition, 1974. Up to 50 copies free. Publications Division, American Foundation for the Blind, 15 West Sixteenth Street, New York, NY 10011.

Toilet Training Your Retarded Child
Leaflet: 8pp. #20-6. By Molly C. Gorelick, Ed.D. Describes practical steps parents can take in toilet training retarded children. Topics covered include the child's ability, parental attitudes, signposts of readiness, procedures, routines, and reward techniques. 20¢. National Association for Retarded Citizens, P.O. Box 6109, Arlington, TX 76011.

Understanding Children Who Are Partially Seeing
Booklet. #049-3. $1.50. Special Child Publications Division, Bernie Straub Publishing Co., 4535 Union Bay Place N.E., Seattle, WA 98105.

Understanding the Mongoloid Child
Pamphlet: 12pp. #10-18. By Cyrus W. Stimson, MD. Gives answers to basic questions about Down's Syndrome, including a list of characteristics of mongoloid children and discussions of their cellular differences, care, and treatment. Also explains genetic probabilities and prevention methods. 25¢. National Association for Retarded Citizens, P.O. Box 6109, Arlington, TX 76011.

The Visually Impaired Child—
Growth, Learning, Development—
Infancy to School Age
Book. #8-5104. A broad discussion of the visually impaired child. Gives an overview of activities appropriate for the visually

impaired child. $1.05. American Printing House for the Blind, P.O. Box 6085, Louisville, KY 40206.

Who Is the Visually Handicapped Child?

Pamphlet: 12pp. F547. A large-print pamphlet describing visually handicapped children, their education, and the preparation needed by teachers of the visually handicapped. Includes a list of professional preparation programs. 1969. Up to 50 copies free. Publications Division, American Foundation for the Blind, 15 West Sixteenth Street, New York, NY 10011.

Your Child Has a Learning Disability—
What Is It?

Booklet: 18pp. #D-44. By Beverly S. Williams. A primer for parents and classroom teachers, giving encouragement that a child with a learning disability can become a self-sufficient adult if given understanding, praise, and proper educational training. 25¢. National Easter Seal Society for Crippled Children and Adults, 2023 West Ogden Avenue, Chicago, IL 60612.

Your Child's Play

Booklet: 25pp. #E-18. By Grace Langdon. What toys mean to a child and how they can contribute to family living. 25¢. National Easter Seal Society for Crippled Children and Adults, 2023 West Ogden Avenue, Chicago, IL 60612.

Your Down's Syndrome Child

Pamphlet: 32pp. #10-22. By David Pitt, M.D. Describes what parents can expect in their Down's Syndrome child at each age level from infancy to adulthood. Includes suggestions on coping with specific problems in rearing a Down's Syndrome child. Single copy free. National Association for Retarded Citizens, P. O. Box 6109, Arlington, TX 76011.

Foods and Recipes

Bread in the Making*

Booklet: 16pp, color. A narration, by school children and the baker, of a trip through a modern bakery. This material is designed for the upper elementary grades but may be adapted to meet the needs of the primary child. 1969. 30¢. Nutrition Education Department, American Institute of Baking, 400 East Ontario Street, Chicago, IL 60611.

Cooking and Eating with Children—
A Way to Learn

Booklet: 48pp. ISBN 0-87173-006-5. Stresses the need to provide children with healthful foods and the importance of eating in a friendly climate. Includes a recipe section and a guide on child input (having the child participate in the selection of foods). 1974. $2.50. Association for Childhood Education International, 3615 Wisconsin Avenue N.W., Washington, DC 20016.

Food and Nutrition*

Set. #24240. Natural color pictures of foods needed for basic health, growth and energy. Valuable information for all children, especially the underprivileged. Twelve pictures, twelve resource sheets. $3.75.

Take-home set. #24299. Brings these important pictures into the home. Consists of five full-color miniatures of each picture in the above set, with parent messages on backs. Total of five sets of twelve pictures per set, to serve five students. $2.50. David C. Cook Publishing Co., School Products Division, 850 North Grove Avenue, Elgin, IL 60120.

Ice Cream for You And Me*

Booklet: 24pp. Teacher's guide, 4pp. #B269. This colorful booklet portrays ice cream making in a modern ice cream plant. Through a series of simple experiments, it involves the child in exploring the properties of this dairy food. 40¢. The Food, Nutrition, and Dairy Council, Shadyside Centre, 5100 Centre Avenue, Pittsburgh, PA 15232.

Let's Make Butter*

Activity sheet: 4pp. Teacher's guide. #B056. The child's activity sheet folds into a stage on which the child can use the accompanying puppet to tell about milk and butter. The teacher's guide includes instructions for making butter in the classroom, artwork, activities, and references. 12¢. The Food, Nutrition, and Dairy Council, Shadyside Centre, 5100 Centre Avenue, Pittsburgh, PA 15232.

Uncle Jim's Dairy Farm*

Booklet: 24pp. Teacher's guide, 2pp. #B284. (For corresponding film, see "Audiovisual" section.) This booklet provides an opportunity both to enrich the child's understanding of daily living on a diary farm and to help the youngster grasp the importance of food for good health. 30¢. The Food, Nutrition, and Dairy Council, Shadyside Centre, 5100 Centre Avenue, Pittsburgh, PA 15232.

Where We Get Our Food*

Booklet: 20pp. Teacher's guide, 4pp. #B125. Explains where we get our dairy foods, fruits and vegetables, eggs, cereals, and meats. Artwork depicts foods in their natural environments and workers who help bring the foods to us. 45¢. The Food, Nutrition, and Dairy Council, Shadyside Centre, 5100 Centre Avenue, Pittsburgh, PA 15232.

Games and Sports

Classroom Activities

Book: 64pp. #245-07000. Games, stunts, and body mechanics for elementary schools. 1963. $1.50. AAHPER Publications— Sales, 1201 Sixteenth Street N.W., Washington, DC 20036.

A Cooperative Program
in Materials Development
for Very Young Hospitalized Children

Leaflet: 9pp. #A-237. By Gloria F. Wolinsky. Lists safe and sturdy, but inexpensive, items created or adapted for use by child care workers in exposing hospitalized infants and toddlers to tactile, visual, auditory, and kinesthetic stimulation. 25¢. National Easter Seal Society for Crippled Children and Adults, 2023 West Ogden Avenue, Chicago, IL 60612.

Easy-to-do Toys and Activities
for Infants and Toddlers

Booklet: 42pp, illustrated. #54. By Beverly Upchurch. Discusses homemade toys, activities, records, action songs and rhymes, mobiles, and wall decorations. Includes a listing of materials and where to get them. $1.50. Day Care and Child Development Council of America, 1012 Fourteenth Street N.W., Washington, DC 20005.

Games for Special Days

Booklet: 48pp. #346. Nearly 140 games for special days and holidays. Some experiences emphasize language arts, social studies, and physical activities. $1.95. The Instructor Publications, Inc., Dansville, NY 14437.

Indoor Games for All Grades

Booklet: 48pp. #387. Group games, combative activities, hopscotch games, relays, stunts, and calisthenics. Includes activities for all levels. $1.95. The Instructor Publications, Inc., Dansville, NY 14437.

Learning Materials Notebook

Notebook. Illustrated. #31. Suggested designs and materials for homemade equipment, toys, and supplies for use with preschool children, both indoors and outdoors. $2.00. Day Care and Child Development Council of America, 1012 Fourteenth Street N.W., Washington, DC 20005.

Let's Play Outdoors

Booklet: 35pp. #101. By Katherine Read Baker. Discusses outdoor play areas, equipment, and the role of the teacher in making outdoor play a rich and satisfying experience. 1966. $1.00. National Association for the Education of Young Children, 1834 Connecticut Avenue N.W., Washington, DC 20009.

Planning Playgrounds for Day Care

Booklet: 38pp., photos. #B-10. Includes three case histories offering models for creating playgrounds: parent-and-staff-built, professional-consultant-built, and child-built. Gives culled wisdom on site, organization, surface, equipment, and role of adults. $2.00. Day Care and Child Development Council of America, 1012 Fourteenth Street N.W., Washington, DC 20005.

Play: The Child Strives toward Self-Realization

Book: 72 pp. #129. Georgianna Engstrom, editor. Examines the young child's natural drive to play. Child development scholars discuss the role and meaning of play as a critically important part of the child's total development. Offers suggestions on the role of adults in facilitating play. Includes theory, research, and a statement of basic issues. 1971. $2.50. National Association for the Education of Young Children, 1834 Connecticut Avenue N.W., Washington, DC 20009.

Playgrounds for City Children

Book: 56pp. #32. A refreshing look at creative playgrounds developed by a contemporary landscape architect. Of interest to all who are responsible for planning playgrounds. $1.50. Day Care and Child Development Council of America, 1012 Fourteenth Street N.W., Washington, DC 20005.

Preschool Games and Activities

Book: 110pp. #ISBN-0-8224-5605-2. By Sandra Taetzsch and Lyn Taetzsch. Helps children develop skills and concepts to make the transition from preschool to school easier. Areas include the child's world, table games, physical activities, numbers and letters, and crafts. 1974. $3.00. Fearon Publishers, Inc., 6 Davis Drive, Belmont, CA 94002.

Rainy Day Games and Activities

Booklet: 48pp. #338. About 200 craft projects and games for fall, winter, and spring at three levels. $1.95. The Instructor Publications, Inc., Dansville, NY 14437.

Teaching Aids and Toys
for Handicapped Children

Book: 62pp. By Barbara Dorwood. Describes the construction and use of teaching aids and toys that have been useful to teachers of handicapped children. Gives ideas for developing similar materials. $3.05. Council for Exceptional Children, 1411 South Jefferson Davis Highway, Suite 900, Arlington, VA 22202.

Toy Buying Guide for Grown-Ups

Booklet. Discusses and illustrates the selection of toys for pre-school and early childhood youngsters. Mattel, Inc., 5150 Rosecrans Avenue, Hawthorne, CA 90230.

Travel Games

Booklet. Describes games and contests that can be played while traveling. For all members of the family. 50¢. The Beavers, Star Route, Laporte, MN 56461.

Tricycles

Fact sheet. #15. Single copy free. U.S. Consumer Product Safety Commission, Washington, DC 20207.

Toys, Games, and Apparatus

Leaflet: 6pp. #B-16. By Gladys Gage Rogers. Describes education, play, and exercise having therapeutic value. 10¢. National Easter Seal Society for Crippled Children and Adults, 2023 West Ogden Avenue, Chicago, IL 60612.

Your Child's Play
Booklet: 25pp. #E-18. By Grace Langdon. What toys mean to a
child and how they can contribute to family living. 25¢. National
Easter Seal Society for Crippled Children and Adults, 2023 West
Ogden Avenue, Chicago, IL 60612.

Guidance

Are You His/Her Type?
Leaflet. #9-0006. Discusses Rh blood incompatibility; emphasizes the life-saving potential of new serum; explains the
needs of some babies of sensitized mothers. The National Foundation, March of Dimes, P.O. Box 2000, White Plains, NY
10602.

Communication: Parents, Children, Teachers
Book: 76pp. How to improve education by improving relationships. Discusses orientation to school, homework, guidance,
report cards, and parent-community roles. 1969. $1.75. Associa-
tion for Childhood Education International, 3615 Wisconsin
Avenue N.W., Washington, DC 20016.

**Counseling the Parent
of the Brain Damaged Child**
Leaflet: 3pp. #A-205. By Ray H. Barsch. Discusses a counseling
program, outlines its objectives, and gives detailed information
about the role of the counselor. 10¢. National Easter Seal Society for Crippled Children and Adults, 2023 West Ogden
Avenue, Chicago, IL 60612.

Do You Really Understand Self-Demand?
Reprint. #752. Dr. Edith B. Jackson answers questions about a
feeding method that puzzles many new mothers. A mother

whose thinking is clear on schedules vs. self-demand will avoid a great deal of needless worry. 20¢. *Baby Talk* Magazine, 66 East Thirty-fourth Street, New York, NY 10016.

Feedback from the Family of Man:
Guidance Pointers from Parents
of Disabled Children

Leaflet: 8pp. #A-220. By Isabel P. Robinault. Letters from parents of handicapped children indicate their needs for information services. 1968. 15¢. National Easter Seal Society for Crippled Children and Adults, 2023 West Ogden Avenue, Chicago, IL 60612.

Genetic Counseling

Booklet. #9-0022. Explains the "why" and "how" of genetic conditions. For families referred to genetic counselors and for allied health workers. The National Foundation, March of Dimes, P.O. Box 2000, White Plains, NY 10602.

Getting an Abortion

Booklet: 16pp. For women who want information on how abortions are done, where to go for counseling and referral, various methods of early and late abortions, cost, and post-abortion care. 35¢. New Readers Press, P.O. Box 131, Syracuse, NY 13210.

A Guide to Discipline

Booklet: 32pp. #302. By Jeanette Galambos Stone. What do you do when a child bites? hits? runs around? This teacher-author takes the reader beyond the usual concerns for rules and regulations, punishments and rewards, to the implications of effective discipline in teacher-child interaction, program planning, and teacher techniques. A forthright approach to the inevitable problems in working with children. 1969. $1.50. National Association for the Education of Young Children, 1834 Connecticut Avenue N.W., Washington, DC 20009.

Help for Your Troubled Child

Booklet. #454. By Alicerose Barman and Lisa Cohen. A parent's guide to psychotherapy. How can parents determine when a child may need professional help for emotional problems? What kinds of help are available? What happens in treatment? How does treatment affect other members of the family? 35¢. Public Affairs Committee, Inc., 381 Park Avenue South, New York, NY 10016.

How to Discipline Your Children

Booklet. #154. By Dorothy Baruch. Describes the basic rules of discipline. Helps the parent apply them to suit the child's personality and age. 35¢. Public Affairs Committee, Inc., 381 Park Avenue South, New York, NY 10016.

"I Won't! I Won't!"

Booklet: 32pp. Illustrates children in problem situations, revealing possible signs of underlying emotional difficulties. Suggests ways of meeting their emotional and physical needs and lists reliable sources of help and guidance. For parents, teachers, health professionals, and others concerned with children. Health and Welfare Division, Metropolitan Life Insurance Company, 1 Madison Avenue, New York, NY 10010.

Let's Be Specific

Leaflet: 4pp. An instrument of introspection to help teachers evaluate their own attitudes and approaches in developing the sense of worth of every child. Stimulates positive thinking. 20¢; $1.00 for 8 copies. Association for Childhood Education International, 3615 Wisconsin Avenue N.W., Washington, DC 20016.

The Mother Who Works outside the Home

Book: 79pp. By Sally Wendkos Olds. A valuable reference covering every aspect of the working mother's concerns. 1975. $1.50 plus 50¢ for postage and service. Child Study Press, 50 Madison Avenue, New York, NY 10010.

Multi-Ethnic Reading
and Audio-Visual Materials for Young Children:
Annotated Bibliography

Pamphlet: 12pp. #101. Lists, according to ethnic groups, good reading and visual materials for reinforcing self-awareness and cultural pride in young children. Materials also educate children in such areas as math, color concept, alphabet, and so forth. Lists publishers and costs of materials. 25¢. Day Care and Child Development Council of America, 1012 Fourteenth Street N.W., Washington, DC 20005.

Parents and Teachers Together:
A Training Manual for Parent Involvement
in Head Start Centers

Book: 84pp, illustrated. #34. Prepared to help groups of parents and teachers work together to develop the type of program they want for their center. Training experiences include helping members become acquainted with each other, assisting members in sharing knowledge and ideas with one another, and helping a group to determine interests and activities to explore. $2.50. Day Care and Child Development Council of America, 1012 Fourteenth Street N.W., Washington, DC 20005.

A Physician Helps You Understand
a Baby's Thumbsucking

Reprint. #750. By Dr. T. Berry Brazelton. Some straight talk about a common parent-puzzler. It gives reassuring and detailed answers to many questions parents ask. 20¢. *Baby Talk* Magazine, 66 East Thirty-fourth Street, New York, NY 10016.

Preschool Teacher's Kit

Idea sheets. #30718. Designed to improve rapport. Folder has twelve idea sheets for children, plus six for their parents. $2.50. David C. Cook Publishing Co., School Products Division, 850 North Grove Avenue, Elgin, IL 60120.

The Rabbit Brothers*

Booklet: 34pp. #C501. Robert Kraus. A humorous cartoon booklet about twin rabbits. Joe, who dislikes all rabbits different from himself, is miserable. But George, who tries to find some good in all rabbits, is much happier. A discussion guide is available for teachers. 35¢. (A filmstrip is also available at $2.50.) Anti-Defamation League of B'Nai B'Rith, 315 Lexington Avenue, New York, NY 10016.

The Shy Child

Pamphlet. #239. By Helen Ross. The causes of shyness are many and may vary with different children. Recognizing that shyness often leads to undue concern, this booklet points out how shy children can be helped by parents and teachers. 35¢. Public Affairs Committee, Inc., 381 Park Avenue South, New York, NY 10016.

A Story about You*

Booklet: 44pp. #244-06854. Discusses normal growth and development. For elementary age children. Revised 1971. $1.00. AAHPER Publications—Sales, 1201 Sixteenth Street N.W., Washington, DC 20036.

Television—How to Use It Wisely with Children

Booklet. By Josette Frank. A practical guide to good management of television viewing. 1976. $2.00 plus 50¢ for postage and service. Child Study Press, 50 Madison Avenue, New York, NY 10010.

Unwed Mother

Booklet: 24pp. Discusses the alternatives of adoption, abortion, temporary foster care, marrying the father, or raising the baby as a single parent. Useful for the girl's parents and for the baby's father, too. 50¢. New Readers Press, P.O. Box 131, Syracuse, NY 13210.

The Why and How of Discipline

Booklet: 36pp. By Aline B. Auerback. Discusses some of the ordinary, everyday problems parents face in bringing up a child. Explains discipline as something parents do *for* and *with* children, not *to* them. 1969. $1.25 plus 50¢ for postage and service. Child Study Press, 50 Madison Avenue, New York, NY 10010.

You and Your Adopted Child

Pamphlet. #274. By Edna J. LeShan. Discusses the concerns of couples who adopt children. A guide for explaining to a child that he or she is adopted and for answering questions. 35¢. Public Affairs Committee, Inc., 381 Park Avenue South, New York, NY 10016.

You, Your Child, and Drugs

Book: 72 pp. A thorough introduction to the subject of children and drugs. $1.50 plus 50¢ for postage and service. Child Study Press, 50 Madison Avenue, New York, NY 10010.

Your Child's Sense of Responsibility

Booklet. #254. By Edith G. Neisser. Describes ways parents can teach their children to be trustworthy, reliable, and responsible members of the family. 35¢. Public Affairs Committee, Inc., 381 Park Avenue South, New York, NY 10016.

Health

Activities That Teach Health

Booklet: 48pp. #342. About sixty activities for dental health, grooming, nutrition, mental health, and so on. $1.95. The Instructor Publications, Inc., Dansville, NY 14437.

Allergic Contact Rashes

Booklet: 6pp. #OP-239. Lists common household items that may cause rashes. 25¢. American Medical Association, Health Education Materials, 535 Dearborn Street, Chicago, IL 60610.

Allergies

Booklet: 6pp. #OP-7. Describes common allergies; tells how the allergic person and the doctor can control them. 15¢. American Medical Association, Health Education Materials, 535 Dearborn Street, Chicago, IL 60610.

Allergy

Pamphlet: 14pp. Discusses asthma, hay fever, and other allergies. Single copy free. Allergy Foundation of America, 801 Second Avenue, New York, NY 10017.

Artificial Ventilation

Card: 2½ " × 4". #OP-55. Describes the latest approved method of artificial respiration. 25¢. American Medical Association, Health Education Materials, 535 Dearborn Street, Chicago, IL 60610.

Bookmark*

#9-0058. A colorful reminder to protect tomorrow's children by caring about our own personal environment—our health. Designed for children. The National Foundation, March of Dimes, P.O. Box 2000, White Plains, NY 10602.

Can You Give First Aid?

Booklet: 32pp. This easy handbook discusses what to do before the doctor comes: the first-aid box, bleeding, shock, when breathing stops, broken bones, burns, bites, and poisons. 50¢. New Readers Press, P.O. Box 131, Syracuse, NY 13210.

The Case for Protective Lenses

Leaflet. #G112. Describes impact-resistant lenses and discusses their advantages and limitations. Written for the general public.

Single copy free. Kentucky Society for the Prevention of Blindness, 301 Heyburn Building, Louisville, KY 40202.

Charlie Brown, Detective
Leaflet. #G116. Tips for parents on children's vision and eye problems, stressing early detection. Explains various functions of eye care professionals. Single copy free. Kentucky Society for the Prevention of Blindness, 301 Heyburn Building, Louisville, KY 40202.

Check Your Child's Vision
Pamphlet: 4pp. Gives a checklist of symptoms easily observed by parents that may indicate that a child has vision problems. Single copy free. Public Information Divison, American Optometric Association, 7000 Chippewa Street, St. Louis, MO 63119.

Crossed Eyes: A Needless Handicap
Leaflet. #G106. Gives description, signs, symptoms, causes, and treatments of the condition. Single copy free. Kentucky Society for the Prevention of Blindness, 301 Heyburn Building, Louisville, KY 40202.

Do You Know These Facts
about Color Deficiency?
Pamphlet: 4pp, illustrated in color. Defines and explains color deficiency in concise, easily understood terms. Includes Dvorine Pseudo-Isochromatic Plates. Single copy free. Public Information Division, American Optometric Association, 7000 Chippewa Street, St. Louis, MO 63119.

Epilepsy School Alert
Folder. Contains various materials to help alert teachers and elementary and secondary students to the facts about epilepsy. Epilepsy Foundation of America, 1828 L Street N.W., Washington, DC 20036.

Eye Trouble in Children

Leaflet. #G102. Tells what signs to look for when children have trouble with their eyes. Single copy free. Kentucky Society for the Prevention of Blindness, 301 Heyburn Building, Louisville, KY 40202.

Family Medical Record

#9-0005. A simple, comprehensive form for keeping vital family health information. The National Foundation, March of Dimes, P.O. Box 2000, White Plains, NY 10602.

Fast Facts about Sickle Cell Anemia

Leaflet, illustrated. #9-0001. Gives questions and answers about this hereditary blood disease and about the activities of the National Foundation in research and education. The National Foundation, March of Dimes, P.O. Box 2000, White Plains, NY 10602.

First Aid Facts Wall Chart

Chart. Includes an emergency telephone list and first aid facts concerning the six basic emergencies which occur most frequently. Johnson & Johnson, Health Care Division, New Brunswick, NJ 08903.

First Aid for Little People*

Pamphlet: 15pp. Simple first aid instructions. Johnson & Johnson, Health Care Division, New Brunswick, NJ 08903.

Health and Cleanliness*

Set. #24224. Helps children learn and practice proper habits for good health and hygiene. Twelve natural color pictures and twelve resource sheets containing facts, background, class activities, stories, questions, and goals. $3.75.

Take-home set. #24307. Five full-color miniatures of each picture in the above set, with messages on backs for parents. $2.50. David C. Cook Publishing Co., School Products Division, 850 North Grove Avenue, Elgin, IL 60120.

Health Appraisal of School Children

Book: 56pp. #OP-187. Sets standards for determining the health status of school children through the cooperation of parents, teachers, physicians, dentists, nurses, and others. Discusses medical and dental examinations and screening tests, and gives sample forms for recording health appraisal data. $2.00. American Medical Association, Health Education Materials, 535 Dearborn Street, Chicago, IL 60610.

Health Appraisal of School Children

Booklet: 40pp. #244-08058. Gives standards for determining the health status of school children. 1970. $1.25. AAHPER Publications—Sales, 1201 Sixteenth Street N.W., Washington, DC 20036.

Home Eye Test

Leaflet. Materials and instructions for home vision screening of preschoolers. Also available in Spanish. Single copy free. Kentucky Society for the Prevention of Blindness, 301 Heyburn Building, Louisville, KY 40202.

Immunization

Booklet: 8pp. #OP-19. Discusses diseases for which there are immunizations. 20¢. American Medical Association, Health Education Materials, 535 Dearborn Street, Chicago, IL 60610.

Insect Stings

Pamphlet: 8pp. Discusses basic facts, types of reaction, toxic reactions, emergency treatment, preventive treatment, and precautions. 35¢. Allergy Foundation of America, 801 Second Avenue, New York, NY 10017.

A Letter to You, Mother, about Measles and Your Child

Pamphlet: 4pp. #OP-138. Tells when and why you should have your infant vaccinated. Lists the complications of measles. 15¢. American Medical Association, Health Education Materials, 535 Dearborn Street, Chicago, IL 60610.

Looking for Health

Booklet: 32pp. A professional reference for people working with children—teachers, administrators, nurses, and other school health personnel. Photographs illustrate clues to illnesses and chronic health problems often seen among school children. Emphasizes the teacher's role as a health observer and the importance of communication and cooperation among home, school, and community. Includes a reference list. Health and Welfare Division, Metropolitan Life Insurance Company, 1 Madison Avenue, New York, NY 10010.

Make Sure Your Child Has Two Good Eyes

Booklet: 6pp. #G107. Tells about good vision. Explains how to take good care of the eyes. Single copy free. Kentucky Society for the Prevention of Blindness, 301 Heyburn Building, Louisville, KY 40202.

Memo to Parents about Immunization

Booklet: 12pp. Explains the importance of early immunizations and gives a suggested schedule. A comprehensive chart details information on the communicable diseases of childhood. Space for keeping children's immunization records is included. Health and Welfare Division, Metropolitan Life Insurance Company, 1 Madison Avenue, New York, NY 10010.

The Orinda Study

Reprint: 16pp. Describes an interprofessional approach to school vision screening, including recommendations for establishing local school screening programs. 25¢. Public Information Division, American Optometric Association, 7000 Chippewa Street, St. Louis, MO 63119.

The Place of Vision in Child Behavior

Leaflet. Explains that some child behavior problems may be caused by vision problems which can be detected in thorough vision examination and corrected by vision therapy. Single copy free. Public Information Division, American Optometric Association, 7000 Chippewa Street, St. Louis, MO 63119.

Poison Plant Rashes

Booklet: 8pp. #OP-25. Describes the poison ivy plant, the rash, and recommended treatment. 25¢. American Medical Association, Health Education Materials, 535 Dearborn Street, Chicago, IL 60610.

Professor Ludwig von Drake's I.Q.

Leaflet. #G114. True and false "Eye-Q" questions on eye health and safety. Single copy free. Kentucky Society for the Prevention of Blindness, 301 Heyburn Building, Louisville, KY 40202.

Q. and A.

Pamphlet. Questions and answers about allergy and allergic diseases. Single copy free. Allergy Foundation of America, 801 Second Avenue, New York, NY 10017.

Rh Disease—A Blood Destroying Anemia of the Newborn

Booklet: 4pp. #OP-237. Tells how Rh disease can affect the unborn child. Explains method of treatment. 20¢. American Medical Association, Health Education Materials, 535 Dearborn Street, Chicago, IL 60610.

The Skin and Its Allergies

Pamphlet: 8pp. Discusses eczema, hives and giant swellings, contact allergy, drug reactions, and other skin allergies. 60¢. Allergy Foundation of America, 801 Second Avenue, New York, NY 10017.

Suggested School Health Policies

Booklet: 40pp. #OP-203. For persons concerned with the health of school children. Discusses policies affecting the health of pupils and personnel in schools, such as food services, emergency medical care, and physical education programs. 65¢. American Medical Association, Health Education Materials, 535 Dearborn Street, Chicago, IL 60610.

Teacher's Guide to Vision Problems
Pamphlet. Gives symptoms of various visual difficulties that can be observed in the classroom. Includes a checklist of symptoms. Single copy free. American Optometric Association, 7000 Chippewa Street, St. Louis, MO 63119.

Tonsils and Adenoids
Booklet: 6pp, illustrated. #OP-174. Explains the purpose of tonsils and adenoids, what they look like, why they are removed, and how to prepare a child for this operation. 20¢. American Medical Association, Health Education Materials, 535 Dearborn Street, Chicago, IL 60610.

Vision: Its Place in the World of Children
Booklet: 28pp. A report on the 1970 White House Conference. $1.50. American Optometric Association, 7000 Chippewa Street, St. Louis, MO 63119.

VD: It Could Happen to You
Booklet: 16pp. Although it emphasizes symptoms, treatment, and prevention of the major venereal diseases, syphilis and gonorrhea, this booklet goes beyond other publications to deal with other venereal diseases that are a growing problem and with nonvenereal conditions that can frighten and upset the uninformed. 28¢. New Readers Press, P.O. Box 131, Syracuse, NY 13210.

Watching Your Child's Health
Leaflet: 8pp. Offers suggestions on what parents can do for their children's health. Discusses the roles of the teacher, other school health personnel, the physician, and the dentist. Health and Welfare Division, Metropolitan Life Insurance Company, 1 Madison Avenue, New York, NY 10010.

What is Astigmatism?
Pamphlet: 4pp. Concise, easily understood definition of this common vision condition. Single copy free. Public Information

Division, American Optometric Association, 7000 Chippewa Street, St. Louis, MO 63119.

What We Do Day by Day*

Prints. #B022. This portfolio consists of twelve full-color pictures showing health practices for young children. Photographs include children from various ethnic groups and economic levels, living in city and suburbs. Teacher's guide is on back of each print. $2.00. The Food, Nutrition, and Dairy Council, Shadyside Centre, 5100 Centre Avenue, Pittsburgh, PA 15232.

When Your Child Is Sick

Booklet. #441. By Jacquiline Seaver. Offers specific guidance and underscores the importance of heeding medical advice. Explains what to do and when to call the doctor. 35¢. Public Affairs Committee, Inc., 381 Park Avenue South, New York, NY 10016.

Your Child's First Vision Examination

Booklet: 12pp. Offers suggestions to parents so they may insure that their child cooperates with the doctor and enjoys this first vision examination. Includes a catchy song, "Animal Eyes." Single copy free. Public Information Division, American Optometric Association, 7000 Chippewa Street, St. Louis, MO 63119.

Your Child's Sight—How You Can Help

Leaflet. #G108. Tells why early eye problems can be difficult to recognize, gives clues to trouble, advises best defenses. Common disorders are also described. Single copy free. Kentucky Society for the Prevention of Blindness, 301 Heyburn Building, Louisville, KY 40202.

Your Health—How Can You Help?*

Booklet: 16pp. Teacher's guide, 4pp. #B086. Emphasizes health practices for children. Questions help involve children in finding out how they can keep their bodies healthy. The teacher's guide offers specific suggestions for use of each section of the booklet. 20¢. The Food, Nutrition, and Dairy Council, Shadyside Centre, 5100 Centre Avenue, Pittsburgh, PA 15232.

Hobbies and Handicrafts

Arts and Crafts for Slow Learners
Booklet: 48pp. #379. How to develop creativity with slow learners. Ideas for picture-making, gifts, and so on. $1.95. The Instructor Publications, Inc., Dansville, NY 14437.

Bits and Pieces:
Imaginative Uses for Children's Learning
Book: 72pp. Recycling of finds, leftovers, giveways, and throwaways for creative learning in class and at home. 1967. $2.00. Association for Childhood Education International, 3615 Wisconsin Avenue N.W., Washington, DC 20016.

Creative Arts and Crafts
Booklet: 44pp, illustrated. #3024. Carefully selected arts and crafts activities that can be done at home or at school. General in nature, these activities can be applied in grades one through six. $1.95. Instructional Fair, Inc., 4158 Lake Michigan Drive, Grand Rapids, MI 49504.

Creating with Materials for Work and Play
Leaflets (12). Discusses various media and materials and building learning from them. Practical, useful ideas for art, dance, science, drama, and so forth. 1969. $2.00. Association for Childhood Education International, 3615 Wisconsin Avenue N.W., Washington, DC 20016.

Cut Yourself a Bunch of Fun
Booklet: 20pp, illustrated. Gives complete directions and patterns for making large decorative flowers. Includes a section of hints and skills. 25¢. Dennison Manufacturing Company, Framingham, MA 01701.

Easy Crafts for the Classroom
Booklet: 48pp. #315. Classroom-tested crafts—weaving, printing, mobiles, casting, and so on. $1.95. The Instructor Publications, Inc., Dansville, NY 14437.

Fun with Sta Flo Liquid Starch

Pamphlet: 15pp. Presents creative and practical suggestions within the basic principles of free expression for all youngsters. Single copy free. A.E. Staley Manufacturing Co., Oak Brook, IL 60521.

Gifts Children Can Make

Booklet: 48pp. #337. Describes 120 gift ideas for every occasion. $1.95. The Instructor Publications, Inc., Dansville, NY 14437.

Move Over Michelangelo

Pamphlet: 6pp. Instructions on how to create your own gifts, decorations, and jewelry with Play Clay. Single copy free; requests should include a stamped, self-addressed envelope. Play Clay, Church and Dwight Company, Inc., 2 Pennsylvania Plaza, New York, NY 10001.

Rags to Riches with Mod Podge

Booklet. Includes many projects for the elementary school child. (Mod podge is a product used in decoupage.) $2.00. Connoisseur Studio, Inc., P.O. Box 7187, Louisville, KY 40207.

Recycle

Booklet: 44pp. Instructions for recycling projects with young children. $1.00 plus 30¢ for postage and handling. Teacher Shop, Children's Museum, Jamaica Way, Boston, MA 02130.

The Scrap Book: A Collection of Activities for Preschoolers

Book: 138pp, illustrated, indexed. #45. Includes games, simple gardening, arts, crafts, perception stimulation, preparation and sensing of foods, simple exercises, and play for three- to five-year-olds. Household scraps are recycled to reduce costs. Emphasis on child initiation. $2.00. Day Care and Child Development Council of America, 1012 Fourteenth Street N.W., Washington, DC 20005.

Scrap Craft

Booklet: 48pp. #348. Creative craft experiences for all grades. Projects use fifty varieties of common scrap materials. $1.95. The Instructor Publications, Inc., Dansville, NY 14437.

Sterling Salt Fun

Leaflet. Gives complete instructions on how to make beads, belts, useful ceramic ash trays and bowls, coral plants, and decorations for Easter and Christmas. Single copy free. International Salt Company, Clarks Summit, PA 18411.

Still More Recipes for Fun

Booklet: 48pp. Crafts, learning games, dramatic play, reading and math readiness, science experiments, and gift ideas. $2.50. PAR Project, Dept. PT, 464 Central Avenue, Northfield, IL 60093.

Holidays

Children Around the World*

Set. #30650. Takes youngsters on an exciting picture tour around the world to learn about the lives of children in other lands: play, home life, clothing, customs, schools, food, housing, and major holidays. Twelve full-color pictures from original art and a 32-page teacher's manual with comprehensive background material, stories, poetry, learning activities, and other resources. $3.75. David C. Cook Publishing Co., School Products Division, 850 North Grove Avenue, Elgin, IL 60120.

Christmas Creativity

Booklet: 13pp. Ideas for family craft projects that brighten the home for the Christmas holidays. Single copy free. Consumer

Products Division, Borden Chemical Division of Borden, Inc., 180 East Broad Street, Columbus, OH 43215.

Creative Holiday Gift Ideas

Pamphlet: 8pp. Contains directions for holiday gifts of food or of handmade decorative objects using baking soda. Single copy free; request should include a stamped self-addressed envelope. Play Clay, Church and Dwight Company, Inc., 2 Pennsylvania Plaza, New York, NY 10001.

Games for Special Days

Booklet: 48pp. #346. Nearly 140 games for special days and holidays. Some experiences emphasize language arts, social studies, and physical activities. $1.95. The Instructor Publications, Inc., Dansville, NY 14437.

Holiday Art

Booklet: 48pp. #324. More than sixty projects using inexpensive materials. $1.95. The Instructor Publications, Inc., Dansville, NY 14437.

Holiday Art and Displays

Booklet: 48pp. #384. More than eighty display projects that coordinate pupil projects and investigate various media. $1.95. The Instructor Publications, Inc., Dansville, NY 14437.

Holidays*

Flannelboard packet. #30619. Teaches the meanings of six major holidays and provides related activities. Flannelgraph sheets contain twenty-eight full-color pictures; record offers six original songs. With resource sheets. $3.75. David C. Cook Publishing Co., School Products Division, 850 North Grove Avenue, Elgin, IL 60120.

Holidays*

Set. #07005. Colorful pictures of the major holidays convey the spirit and meaning of celebrating these special days. Twelve full-color pictures plus twelve resource sheets supplying facts, questions, aims, things to do, rhythmic activities, and other resources. $3.75. David C. Cook Publishing Co., School Products Division, 850 North Grove Avenue, Elgin, IL 60120.

A Pumpkin in a Pear Tree

Book. Filled with ideas that are easy to do and that call for ingredients that are readily available. Twelve months of holiday fun. $4.95. PAR Project, Dept. PT, 464 Central Avenue, Northfield, IL 60093.

Recipes for Holiday Fun

Booklet: 38pp, illustrated. #42-A. Offers creative ideas for special holiday projects throughout the year. Includes games, party ideas, craft projects, neighborhood get-togethers, and recipes for holiday cooking. $2.50. Day Care and Child Development Council of America, 1012 Fourteenth Street N.W., Washington, DC 20005.

The Story of Your Christmas Tree

Leaflet: 5pp. By Floyd E. Carlson. Includes description of buds, branches, needles, trunk, and wood fibers. Single copy free. State University of New York, College of Environmental Science and Forestry, Syracuse, NY 13210.

Kindergarten and Preschool

(See also Education)

Aides to Teachers and Children

Book: 64pp. Discusses who aides are, what they do, how to find them, and how to train and work with them. Introduction by James L. Hymes, Jr. Includes bibliography. 1968. $1.50. Association for Childhood Education International, 3615 Wisconsin Avenue N.W., Washington, DC 20016.

Arranging the Informal Classroom

Book. By Brenda S. Engel. Help for the classroom teacher who wishes to use the same old furniture and room to create a new learning environment. Indicates possibilities for the use of space, and particularly attempts to describe in practical terms how to rearrange a classroom, allowing always for wide differences in the styles of teacher and students and in the givens of the room. $3.60. EDC Distribution Center, 39 Chapel Street, Newton, MA 02160.

Basic Propositions for Early Childhood Education

Leaflet: 12pp. #33. A statement of basic assumptions and knowledge on which a good program may be planned, and a suggestion of basic guidelines for effective programs. Useful for anyone involved in day care. 25¢. Day Care and Child Development Council of America, 1012 Fourteenth Street N.W., Washington, DC 20005.

Child's Right to Quality Day Care

Leaflet: 8pp. A position paper by Annie L. Butler. Explores the need for day care and what that term includes. Discusses quality, licensing, and responsibility. 1970. 35¢. Association for Childhood Education International, 3615 Wisconsin Avenue N.W., Washington, DC 20016.

Count Fingers, Count Toes*

Book: 38pp. #ISBN-513-0018-6. An introduction to the dynamics of our number system in rhymes and easy style. $2.50. T.S. Denison and Co., 5100 West Eighty-second Street, Minneapolis, MN 55437.

Curriculum Ideas for the Modern Kindergarten

Booklet: 40pp. New aspects of such standard kindergarten activities as block building, art, music, and woodworking. Sections on the teacher's new role, the importance of well-planned field trips, the many ways to get ready for reading, and how science and math are everywhere. $2.50. American Swiss Association, 60 East Forty-second Street, Room 511, New York, NY 10017.

Day Care: What and Why

Booklet: 12pp. Outlines the purposes and programs of quality services for young children, including group day care, family day care, infant group care, nursery schools, and drop-in centers. Offers references for further information. Health and Welfare Division, Metropolitan Life Insurance Company, 1 Madison Avenue, New York, NY 10010.

Early Childhood Education:
An Introduction to the Profession

Book: 72pp. #300. By James L. Hymes, Jr. A complete revision of Hymes's popular review of the status of kindergartens, nursery schools, Head Start, and child care programs, and of the satisfactions that can be derived from working with young children. Includes background information about the growth of the profession and the social forces which have shaped services for young children. 1975. $1.50. National Association for the Education of Young Children, 1834 Connecticut Avenue N.W., Washington, DC 20009.

Handbook for Project Head Start

Booklet: 24pp. G461. Prepared under the direction of Dr. Robert D. Hess, Urban Child Center, University of Chicago. Contains some of the most promising teaching methods in the field of compensatory education. 50¢. Anti-Defamation League of B'Nai B'Rith, 315 Lexington Avenue, New York, NY 10016.

Help: A Handbook for Child Care Workers

Book: 56pp, illustrated. #93. Discusses language development, room arrangement, and a full range of activities. Provides sample daily schedules and lists of materials, recipes, games, and books. $1.75. Day Care and Child Development Council of America, 1012 Fourteenth Street N.W., Washington, DC 20005.

Ideas That Work with Young Children

Book: 236pp. #304. Katherine Read Baker, editor. Thirty-seven articles from *Young Children* provide practical, valuable information for teachers. The seven sections include: understanding children and teaching; setting up a learning environment; language experiences; parents and teachers; areas of special challenge; and consulting with people in other professions. 1973. $3.00. National Association for the Education of Young Children, 1834 Connecticut Avenue N.W., Washington, DC 20009.

The Infant Care Center

Pamphlet: 19pp., illustrated. #30. By Sanford Hirshen and Joe Ouye. Discusses the design of an infant care center. Approached from a thorough review of the literature on the effects of immediate physical environment on infant development. Designed for newborn infants up to 2½ years old. Includes floor plans. $1.50. Day Care and Child Development Council of America, 1012 Fourteenth Street N.W., Washington, DC 20005.

Kindergarten: A Guide for Teaching

Book: 99pp. Educational Service Publication #33. By Betty Ann Roth. Gives basic ideas and principles on teaching at the preschool level. 1972. $1.50. Extension Service, University of Northern Iowa, Cedar Falls, IA 50613.

Learning about Numbers*

Flannelboard packet. #44685. Youngsters learn to recognize numbers, then use them to count objects and make comparisons (more-less, big-little). Forty-nine flannelboard figures—calendar, clock, large numerals, coins, and objects of various kinds. Record with six songs; resource sheets. $3.75. David C. Cook Publishing Co., School Products Division, 850 North Grove Avenue, Elgin, IL 60120.

The Learning Process

Pamphlet. 1011-6-1J. Answers these questions: What do we learn? When are children ready to learn? What is the right answer? What do children see? Why is practice necessary? 75¢. National Education Association Order Dept., The Academic Building, Saw Mill Road, West Haven, CT 06516.

Listening

Pamphlet. #1012-4-1J. Provides a variety of exercises at all levels to heighten listening power in the three related stages: hearing sounds, distinguishing understandable words, and extracting meaning. 75¢. National Education Association Order Dept., The Academic Building, Saw Mill Road, West Haven, CT 06516.

The Logic of Action

Book. By Frances Hawkins. A record of the author's experiences in an urban school. As an illustration of creative teaching, this book has much to offer the teachers of all children. $3.60. EDC Distribution Center, 39 Chapel Street, Newton, MA 02160.

Montessori in Perspective

Book: 80pp. #117. Edited by the Publications Committee, Lucile C. Perryman, Chairman. The writings and methods of Maria Montessori are analyzed by a number of prominent educators. Discusses the advantages and disadvantages of the Montessori approach in terms of what is known today about the growth and development of young children. 1966. $2.00. National Association for the Education of Young Children, 1834 Connecticut Avenue N.W., Washington, DC 20009.

Nursery School Portfolio

Leaflets (16). The whys and wherefores of nursery school. Leaflets cover many aspects of early learning: programs, observation, evaluation, discipline, and so forth. 1969. $2.25. Association for Childhood Education International, 3615 Wisconsin Avenue N.W., Washington, DC 20016.

The Purple Picker-Upper*

Manual: 16pp. #35956. Preschoolers, kindergarteners, and first graders learn about helpfulness, good manners, and cleanliness from the Purple Octopus and his whimsical friends. Ten colorful pictures introduce Petunia the Parent Helper, George Go-to-Bed Bear, Sherman a Shark Who Shares, Terry Turn-Taking Turtle, Alice Tooth-Brushing Alligator, Walter Well-Washed Walrus, Dora Dress-Herself Elephant, Myron a Well-Mannered Moose, Herschel the Hair-Combing Hound, and the star, Peter the Purple Picker-Upper! $1.95. David C. Cook Publishing Co., School Products Division, 850 North Grove Avenue, Elgin, IL 60120.

Open Education
Book. An overview discusses the basic concepts of open education and how they relate to the learner, knowledge, and the school society. A second overview stresses the social implications of open education. The final article relates Piaget's theories to classroom practice. $1.20. EDC Distribution Center, 39 Chapel Street, Newton, MA 02160.

Open Education: The Legacy
of the Progressive Movement
Book: 80pp. #120. Georgianna Engstrom, editor. Prominent scholars examine various facets of the open education concept. Current efforts toward active involvement of children in their own learning, especially in the English Infant School, are explored. 1970. $2.00. National Association for the Education of Young Children, 1834 Connecticut Avenue N.W., Washington, DC 20009.

Program Planning Aids for Day Care Centers
Book: 72pp, illustrated. #46. Covers discipline, field trips, books, records, songs, fingerplay, inexpensive homemade equipment, and things to do and make. $2.00. Day Care and Child Development Council of America, 1012 Fourteenth Street N.W., Washington, DC 20005.

A Pre-Primary Program
Book: 50pp. #5046. Sequenced lesson plans, including pretests, posttests, methods, and teacher dialogue, for prereading skill and concept development and beginning numeration skill (to

ten). $1.95. Instructional Fair, Inc., 4158 Lake Michigan Drive, Grand Rapids, MI 49504.

Responding to Individual Needs in Head Start
Book: 93pp., illustrated. HE 1.468. In 2/pt.1 S/N 1792-00016. Designed for Head Start staff, but equally valuable for parents and others involved in child care. Gives advice for teachers who work with children having physical, cognitive, or emotional problems. Suggests ways teachers can assist special children in group situations in which the special child may be meeting non-handicapped children for one of the first times. Describes activities in which blind, mentally retarded, hyperactive, and other special children can participate. Also includes medical information about childhood handicaps and health impairments. 1974. $1.85. U.S. Government Printing Office, Public Documents Dept., Washington, DC 20402.

Sensory Factors in the School
Learning Environment
Booklet. #1021-3-1J. Discusses the factors inherent in present classroom design and identifies those factors necessary for the optimum learning environment. 75¢. National Education Association Order Dept., The Academic Building, Saw Mill Road, West Haven, CT 06516.

Setting Up a Kindergarten
Book. Details are given for the establishment of a preschool program. $1.50. American Swiss Association, 60 East Forty-second Street, Room 511, New York, NY 10017.

Some Ways of Distinguishing a Good Early
Childhood Program
Pamphlet. #402. A guide that can be used to tell a good early childhood program from a poor one. Also available in Spanish. 1 to 24 copies, 25¢ each. 25 to 100 copies, 10¢ each. More than 100 copies, 5¢ each. National Associaton for the Education of Young Children, 1834 Connecticut Avenue N.W., Washington, DC 20009.

Teaching the Disadvantaged

Pamphlet. 1023-X-1J. Answers the following questions: What are the characteristics of the disadvantaged? What are their learning handicaps? What teaching methods are successful with them? What are the problems of each age group? Filmstrip also available. 75¢. National Education Association Order Dept., The Academic Building, Saw Mill Road, West Haven, CT 06516.

A Trip to the Farm*

Set. #24273. Colorful pictures help children to understand farm life and to identify the animals, buildings, and equipment. Deals with crops and harvests, life of a farm child, the animals, and farm duties. Set of twelve full-color pictures and twelve individual resource sheets covering facts and background, suggested aims, questions, learning activities, stories, and other resources. $3.75. David C. Cook Publishing Co., School Products Division, 850 North Grove Avenue, Elgin, IL 60120.

Workshop Procedures

Manual. To be used by leaders in conjunction with "Recipe" books when giving workshops. $2.50. PAR Project, Dept. PT, 464 Central Avenue, Northfield, IL 60093.

Language Development

Bright Promise

Booklet: 21pp. #E-26. By Eugene T. McDonald. Presents information of help to parents of a child with cleft palate. 35¢. National Easter Seal Society for Crippled Children and Adults, 2023 Ogden Avenue, Chicago, IL 60612.

Cartoon Activities*

Book: 52pp. #4037. This colorful grouping of cartoons and language arts experiences builds the child's self-concept and develops creative skills and language abilities. Includes creative writing and linguistic tasks. $1.95. Instructional Fair, Inc., 4158 Lake Michigan Drive, Grand Rapids, MI 49504.

A Child's Right to the Expressive Arts

Booklet: 12pp. A position paper by Arne J. Nixon. Encourages development of environments that allow creativity to flourish; summarizes a child's rights. 1969. 15¢. Association for Childhood Education International, 3615 Wisconsin Avenue N.W., Washington, DC 20016.

Creative Dramatics

Booklet: 48pp. #389. Practical tips and activities, carefully detailed. Covers pantomime, spoken dialogue, and improvisation. $1.95. The Instructor Publications, Inc., Dansville, NY 14437.

Creative Dramatics for All Children

Book: 64pp. By Emily Gillies. Discusses six principles for using creative dramatics. Includes chapters on working with emotionally and physically handicapped and second-language-speaking children. 1973. $3.25. Association for Childhood Education International, 3615 Wisconsin Avenue N.W., Washington, DC 20016.

Finger and Action Rhymes

Booklet: 48pp. #322. Fifty finger plays and action rhymes for holidays, special days, and familiar situations. $1.95. The Instructor Publications, Inc., Dansville, NY 14437.

Fun with Language Arts

Booklet: 48pp. #329. Fun activities to help children feel, think, and express themselves. $1.95. The Instructor Publications, Inc., Dansville, NY 14437.

Helping Your Child Speak Correctly

Booklet. #445. By John E. Bryant. An estimated 5 percent of school age children have serious speech defects, and as many more have minor speech problems. Describes how normal speech develops and shows how to help children learn good speech patterns. Discusses speech disorders and how they can be corrected. 35¢. Public Affairs Committee, Inc., 381 Park Avenue South, New York, NY 10016.

How Babies Learn to Talk
Book: 85pp, illustrated. #142. By Peggy Pizzo and Judy Manning. An easy-to-read, well illustrated parent education booklet spelling out the importance of talking with babies. Describes language development and the family's role in helping it. An appendix gives summaries of language development research. $2.00. Day Care and Child Development Council of America, 1012 Fourteenth Street N.W., Washington, DC 20005.

Improving Listening Skills
Booklet: 48pp. #365. Gives techniques for developing listening skills, plus many activities. Bibliography. $1.95. The Instructor Publications, Inc., Dansville, NY 14437.

Language Games, Levels One, Two, and Three
Booklets: 48pp. each. #4031, 4032, 4033. Animated games and creative activities to develop language skills and concepts. $1.95 each. Instructional Fair, Inc., 4158 Lake Michigan Drive, Grand Rapids, MI 49504.

Language in Early Childhood Education
Book: 134pp. #131. Courtney B. Cazden, editor. Presents suggestions for helping young children develop oral language and relates them to an overview of oral language from early acquisition to learning to read. Includes a critical analysis of currently available language programs. 1972. $3.00. National Association for the Education of Young Children, 1834 Connecticut Avenue N.W., Washington, DC 20009.

Language Learning Activities
for the Disadvantaged Child

Booklet: 36pp. #G473. By Carl Bereiter and Siegfried Engelmann. Gives a number of excellent gamelike activities designed to develop in the disadvantaged child an ability to hear, to understand, and to use language. 60¢. Anti-Defamation League of B'Nai B'Rith, 315 Lexington Avenue, New York, NY 10016.

A Speech Pathologist Talks to the Parents
of a Nonverbal Child

Leaflet: 2pp. #L-80. By Harriet W. Dubner. An open letter that answers basic questions asked by parents of children with delayed speech, whether it be from cerebral palsy, mental retardation, brain damage, or mental disturbance. Single copy free. National Easter Seal Society for Crippled Children and Adults, 2023 West Ogden Avenue, Chicago, IL 60612.

Speech Therapy for the Cerebral Palsied

Book: 62pp. #E-30. By Harold Westlake. Presents step-by-step procedures to estimate a child's language potential and to establish guides for therapy. Discusses principles and approaches to therapy and special techniques. 50¢. National Easter Seal Society for Crippled Children and Adults, 2023 West Ogden Avenue, Chicago, IL 60612.

Stories That Stick*

Booklet: 48pp. #321. Sixteen stories and sixty sketches of people, animals, objects, for use on flannelboard. $1.95. The Instructor Publications, Inc., Dansville, NY 14437.

Stuttering: Its Prevention

Book: 64pp. #3. Written by a group of eminent speech pathologists for parents who do not want their children to stutter, and especially for those parents of very young children who think they have reason to be concerned about their child's speech. 25¢. Speech Foundation of America, 152 Lombardy Road, Memphis, TN 38111.

Treatment of the Young Stutterer in the School

Book: 64pp. #4. An outline of the problems encountered by the speech therapist working with stutterers in the elementary school. Answers questions asked by public school therapists about how to work in therapy with the young stutterer. 25¢. Speech Foundation of America, 152 Lombardy Road, Memphis, TN 38111.

Libraries

Bibliography of Books for Children

Bulletin: 112pp. An annotated list, with titles arranged by age level and subject; major awards noted. An invaluable reference. 1974. $2.75. Association for Childhood Education International, 3615 Wisconsin Avenue N.W., Washington, DC 20016.

Books for Children

Catalog. Lists selected books for children. Bank Street College of Education, Book Store, 610 West 112th Street, New York, NY 10025.

CBC Bookmark

A brief description of the Council's purpose and activities. Free; send stamped, self-addressed envelope. The Children's Book Council, Inc., 67 Irving Place, New York, NY 10003.

Care for Books*

Bookmarks. Red and white bookmarks designed by Hardie Gramatky remind children about the proper handling of books.

Free; send stamped, self-addressed envelope. The Children's Book Council, Inc., 67 Irving Place, New York, NY 10003.

Children's Book Week Artists and Slogans
A mimeographed list of Children's Book Week slogans and poster artists since 1919. The list is introduced by a brief explanation of Book Week. Free; send stamped, self-addressed #10 envelope. The Children's Book Council, 67 Irving Place, New York, NY 10003.

Children's Books and Recordings Suggested as Holiday Gifts
Book. 1975. $2.00. The New York Public Library, Office of Branch Libraries, 8 East Fortieth Street, New York, NY 10016.

Children's Encyclopedias and Sets
Reprint: 10pp. #8389-5258-5. From *The Booklist,* June 15, 1970. Explains the types of children's encyclopedias and how to evaluate them. Gives sources of reviews, names those recommended by *The Booklist.* 25¢. Order Dept., American Library Association, 50 East Huron Street, Chicago, IL 60611.

Choosing a Child's Book
Pamphlet: 4pp. Some fundamentals for parents and nonprofessionals concerned with buying books for children. Includes a short bibliography of selected periodicals and booklists. Free; send stamped, self-addressed #10 envelope. The Children's Book Council, Inc., 67 Irving Place, New York, NY 10003.

Disadvantaged Youth and the Library
Reprint: 24pp. #8389-5208-g. From *Top of the News,* January 1967. Discusses library services for disadvantaged children and young adults. 20¢. Order Dept., American Library Association, 50 East Huron Street, Chicago, IL 60611.

Guide to Children's Magazines, Newspapers, Reference Books
Pamphlet: 12pp. Annotated list designed to acquaint parents and teachers with quality literature. 1974. 50¢ each; 10 copies

$4.00. Association for Childhood Education International, 3615 Wisconsin Avenue N.W., Washington, DC 20016.

How to Organize a Local Showcase Exhibit

Pamphlet: 4pp. Basic suggestions, gathered from the hundreds of communities that have arranged successful exhibits, for organizing a showcase display. List of current showcase titles and available materials enclosed. Single copy free; send stamped, self-addressed #10 envelope. The Children's Book Council, Inc., 67 Irving Place, New York, NY 10003.

International Children's Book Day*

Poster. 11″ × 15″, color. Warm, witty poster based on Hans Christian Andersen's story "The Emperor's New Clothes." Mounted on heavy board with an easel back. $4.95. The Children's Book Council, Inc., 67 Irving Place, New York, NY 10003.

International Children's Book Day

Reprint: 5pp. #8389-5283-6. From *Top of the News,* November 1967. Reports on the observance of International Children's Book Day, sponsored by the International Board on Books for Youth in Ann Arbor, Michigan. Includes suggestions for observance in all libraries. 10¢. Order Dept., American Library Association, 50 East Huron Street, Chicago, IL 60611.

Let's Read Together:
Books for Family Enjoyment

Book: 116pp. #8389-3096-4. An annotated bibliography of about 550 titles, grouped by reader interest and age level, 2–14. 1969. $2.00. Order Dept., American Library Association, 50 East Huron Street, Chicago, IL 60611.

Libraries and Day Care

Folder, illustrated. #8389-5362-X. Shows ways in which libraries can assist day care centers. Prepared by the Library Service to the Disadvantaged Child Committee, CSD. Can be used as a poster. 25¢. Order Dept., American Library Association, 50 East Huron Street, Chicago, IL 60611.

Libros en Expanol
Booklet. An annotated listing of children's books in Spanish. 50¢. The New York Public Library, Office of Branch Libraries, 8 East Fortieth Street, New York, NY 10016.

Literature with Children
Bulletin: 64pp. Explores ways to provide rich and balanced contacts with literature. Discusses use of critiques, records of reading, poetry, choral reading, storytelling, dramatization, and multi-media presentations. Includes teacher resource list. 1972. $2.50. Association for Childhood Education International, 3615 Wisconsin Avenue N.W., Washington, DC 20016.

No Crystal Stair
Book. A bibliography of Black Literature. $2.00. The New York Public Library, Office of Branch Libraries, 8 East Fortieth Street, New York, NY 10016.

Notable Children's Books of 1975
Leaflet. #8389-5262-3. The annual list, reprinted from *American Libraries,* April 1976. 10¢. Order Dept., American Library Association, 50 East Huron Street, Chicago, IL 60611.

Picture Books for Creative Thinking
Booklet: 18pp. Educational Service Publication #36. By Joan Diamond. A bibliography. 1974. $1.00. Extension Service, University of Northern Iowa, Cedar Falls, IA 50613.

Reading with Your Child through Age 5
Booklet: 48pp, illustrated. A guide to selecting books to read aloud to young children. Contains annotated listings of more than 200 books covering a variety of subjects and ethnic groups. 1976. $1.50 plus 50¢ for postage and service. Child Study Press, 50 Madison Avenue, New York, NY 10010.

Selected Media about the American Indian
for Young Children

Booklet. #8389-5353-0. By Suzanne S. Cane and others. Lists children's materials that represent the Indian realistically. Includes audiovisual materials and materials for adults. $1.00. Order Dept., American Library Association, 50 East Huron Street, Chicago, IL 60611.

Sources of Free and Inexpensive Pictures

Booklet: 32pp. #CPS2. Lists all kinds of pictures, many of which are difficult to find. Colorful pictures are available free or at very nominal cost to build a picture file in a variety of subject areas. This is one of the most comprehensive and complete source booklets. 1973. $1.00. Bruce Miller Publications, P.O. Box 369, Riverside, CA 92502.

Sources of Free and Inexpensive Teaching Aids

Booklet: 32pp. #CPS1. This is the twenty-seventh edition of this well-known booklet, whose first edition was published in 1939. It lists hundreds of sources of educational materials, all approved and carefully annotated. For all grade levels including college, sources are listed in almost every field of interest. 1972. $1.00. Bruce Miller Publications, P.O. Box 369, Riverside, CA 92502.

Starting out Right:
Choosing Books about Black People
for Young Children

Book: 96pp. #106. Bettye I. Latimer, editor. Provides a conceptual framework for children's books dealing with blacks by offering guidelines and rationale for examining this new body of literature. Good background for selecting "black-inclusive" books. Bibliography, with each publication critiqued using the criteria the authors provide. $2.00. Day Care and Child

Development Council of America, 1012 Fourteenth Street N.W., Washington, DC 20005.

Winners and Honor Books
for the Newbery and Caldecott Awards

Booklet: 26pp. #8389-5236-4. A complete listing of Newbery and Caldecott winners and honor books from 1922 to date (Newbery Award) and from 1938 to date (Caldecott Award). 50¢. Order Dept., American Library Association, 50 East Huron Street, Chicago, IL 60611.

Motor Development

Cognitive and Readiness Skills

Book: 70pp. #5042. Sequences the most crucial gross muscle skills, identification of body parts, visual tracking, attention training, and classification skills, as well as shape, color, size, and sound discrimination skills. Eighty-five cognitive and prereading skill tasks and creative activities. $3.95. Instructional Fair, Inc., 4158 Lake Michigan Drive, Grand Rapids, MI 49504.

Perceptual Motor Development

Booklets (5): 48pp. each. By Jack J. Capon. This important new series presents successful movement education activities for primary grades. Helps teachers assess students' motor strengths and weaknesses through a series of easily given elemental tests and tasks which require little instruction time. "Basic Movement Activities," #ISBN-0-8224-5300-2. "Ball, Rope, Hoop Activities," #ISBN-0-8224-5301-0. "Balance Activities," #ISBN-0-8224-5302-9. "Beanbag, Rhythm Stick Activities,"

#ISBN-0-8224-5303-7. "Tire, Parachute Activities," #ISBN-0-8224-5304-5. 1975. $3.00 each. Fearon Publishers, Inc., 6 Davis Drive, Belmont CA 94002.

Self Care and Body Usage Skills

Book: 70pp. #5043. Outlines the seventy common gross muscle and related skills necessary for children to care for themselves. Lessons include such items as buttoning, snapping, and controlling the direction of ball when kicking. Each task has a creative teaching suggestion. $3.95. Instructional Fair, Inc., 4158 Lake Michigan Drive, Grand Rapids, MI 49504.

The Significance of the Young Child's Motor Development

Book: 56pp. #128. Georgianna Engstrom, editor. Physical education specialists and early childhood educators join in a pioneering cooperative effort to explore the vital role of motor development in the total development of the young child. Contains excellent suggestions for observation and study of young children. National Association for the Education of Young Children, 1834 Connecticut Avenue N.W., Washington, DC 20009.

Music and Songs

Best Records and Books about Spanish-Speaking Americans

Catalog: 24pp. Selected for truth in history, recognition of contribution, appreciation of culture, and pride in identity. Single copy free. Children's Music Center, 5373 West Pico Boulevard, Los Angeles, CA 90019.

Best Records, Books, and Instruments
for Dance and Dance Therapy

Catalog: 48pp. Single copy free. Children's Music Center, 5373 West Pico Boulevard, Los Angeles, CA 90019.

Best Records and Books for Multi-Ethnic Studies,
Multi-Cultural Education

Catalog: 25pp. Listings selected for truth in history, recognition of contribution, appreciation of culture, and pride in identity. Single copy free. Children's Music Center, 5373 West Pico Boulevard, Los Angeles, CA 90019.

Creative Movement for the Developing Child:
A Nursery School Handbook for Non-Musicians

Book: 88pp. #ISBN-0-8224-1660-3. By Clare Cherry. A complete program of rhythmic activities for the preschool child, written in layman's language. Contains more than 200 goal-directed activities, plus materials for singing, listening, and other musical experiences. Second edition, 1971. $3.00. Fearon Publishers, Inc., 6 Davis Drive, Belmont, CA 94002.

It's a Small, Small World,
but Larger than You Think

Booklet: 44pp. #140. By John Prondzinski and Stanley Roth. Especially designed for nonprofessional musicians and teachers. Provides a training experience in using music to learn, to enjoy, and to move. A participatory workshop format, including a list of resource materials and an excellent bibliography. $2.00. Day Care and Child Development Council of America, 1012 Fourteenth Street N.W., Washington, DC 20005.

Nursery Rhymes*

Set. #30627. Classic favorites: twelve highly interesting and colorful pictures with twelve resource sheets containing rhymes, music learning activities, rhythmic activities, things to do, and facts for teaching. $3.75. David C. Cook Publishing Co., School Products Division, 850 North Grove Avenue, Elgin, IL 60120.

Pentatonic Songs for Young Children
Booklet: 24pp. #ISBN-0-8224-9013-1. These songs may be used for singing, hand singing, rhythmic activities, and the development of "inner hearing." 1967. List 72¢; School 54¢. Fearon Publishers, Inc., 6 Davis Drive, Belmont, CA 94002.

This Little Puffin
Book: 206pp, illustrated. A collection of nursery songs, rhymes, and finger plays for elementary and preschool children. 1969. 95¢. Penguin Books, Inc., 7110 Ambassador Road, Baltimore, MD 21207.

Nutrition

(See also Audiovisual)

Eight Mistaken Ideas about a Toddler's Diet
Reprint. #757. Which foods are really the most important? How about milk? mealtimes? eating habits? Dr. Harold D. Lynch and Dr. William D. Snively, Jr. answer these questions—and explode some far-too-prevalent myths about feeding youngsters. 20¢. *Baby Talk* Magazine, 66 East Thirty-fourth Street, New York, NY 10016.

Every Day . . . Eat the 1-2-3-4 Way*
Poster, #P515. Miniature, #B021. Teacher's guide, 4pp. Illustrations of the four food groups help boys and girls understand the kinds of foods they need for their best growth and health. 50¢ per poster, 5¢ per miniature. Food, Nutrition, and Dairy Council, Shadyside Centre, 5100 Centre Avenue, Pittsburgh, PA 15232.

Feeding Mentally Retarded Children

Leaflet: 12pp. #40-3. By the Children's Bureau. A guide for nurses working with families who have retarded children. Defines areas of nursing concern in teaching the family to help the child. 30¢. National Association for Retarded Citizens, P.O. Box 6109, Arlington, TX 76011.

Flannelboard Stories*

Four stories about snacking, nutrition, ecology, and the environment. $1.00. Consumer Services, Sunkist Growers, Inc., P.O. Box 7888, Van Nuys, CA 91409.

Good Food for the Health of the Mother and Baby during Pregnancy

Placemat. #9-0004. Colorful, educational placemat discussing nutrition and pregnancy. The National Foundation, March of Dimes, P.O. Box 2000, White Plains, NY 10602.

Meals and Snacks for You*

Posters (4). Teacher's guide, 4pp. #P523. Full-color pictures of children eating a nutritious breakfast, lunch, dinner, and a selection of snacks. Designed to encourage discussions of wise food selection by children or parents. The teacher's guide suggests other activities. $1 per set. The Food, Nutrition, and Dairy Council, Shadyside Centre, 5100 Centre Avenue, Pittsburgh, PA 15232.

More Milk, Please!*

Booklet: 20pp. Teacher's guide, 4pp. #B027. Shows youngsters the importance of our milk supply as well as the interdependence of rural and urban areas. Questions involve the child in finding out more about the production, processing, distribution, and consumption of milk. Can be used with the *More Milk, Please* posters. 30¢. Food, Nutrition, and Dairy Council, Shadyside Centre, 5100 Centre Avenue, Pittsburgh, PA 15232.

More Milk, Please!*

Posters (6). Teacher's guide, 2pp. #P501. The bright, colorful posters tell the story of milk from the farm to the city: cows feeding, milking time, taking milk to the city, bottling pasteurized milk, delivering milk to the home, and enjoying milk at every meal. Can be used alone or to introduce the *More Milk, Please* booklet. $1.50. Food, Nutrition, and Dairy Council, Shadyside Centre, 5100 Centre Avenue, Pittsburgh, PA 15232.

One Child—One Chance
Book: 54pp. National report on the Supplemental Food Program. 1974. $1.00. The Children's Foundation, 1028 Connecticut Avenue N.W., Suite 1112, Washington, DC 20036.

Special Food Service Program for Children
Leaflet: 10pp. Explains food assistance for day care centers, Head Start, and recreation programs. 1974. 50¢. The Children's Foundation, 1028 Connecticut Avenue N.W., Suite 1112, Washington, DC 20036.

Parent Education

(See also Audiovisual, Guidance)

And Then There Were Two—
A Handbook for Mothers and Fathers of Twins
Booklet: 45pp. A handbook on the special joys and problems of bringing up children two at a time, based on the first-hand experience of more than 100 parents. Helpful hints for raising twins from infancy through the early years. 1973. $1.50 plus 50¢ for postage and service. Child Study Press, 50 Madison Avenue, New York, NY 10010.

The Baby and the Family
Booklet: 24pp. A birth means adjustments for the whole family: mother, father, other children, and in-laws. Knowing what to expect helps smooth the way. Discusses changes in emotions, in-

terpersonal relationships, family finances, employment, and social life. 50¢. New Readers Press, Box 131, Syracuse, NY 13210.

Baby and Other Teachers

Book: 90pp., illustrated. #141. By May Aaronson and Jean Rosenfeld. This easy-to-read booklet describes infant/toddler-parent/adult relations and their importance to the mental health of the child. Written in bold, simple language with illustrations on each page. 16-page appendix includes more than fifty brief summaries of research studies about child development on which the text is based. $2.25. Day Care and Child Development Council of America, 1012 Fourteenth Street N.W., Washington, DC 20005.

Be Good to Your Baby before It Is Born

Booklet. #9-0002. What every expectant mother wants and needs to know for her baby's health and her own. The National Foundation, March of Dimes, P.O. Box 2000, White Plains, NY 10602.

A Child in the Family

Booklet: 6pp. #OP-30. For new or expectant parents. Discusses bottle and breast feeding, thumbsucking, and the second child. 15¢. American Medical Association, Health Education Materials, 535 North Dearborn Street, Chicago, IL 60610.

Common Causes of Night Crying and Sleeplessness

Reprint. #754. Dr. Gustave Weinfeld discusses almost every kind of baby-sleep question that plagues parents of tiny babies. His suggestions have proved to be a real help in handling this common problem. 20¢. *Baby Talk* Magazine, 66 East Thirty-fourth Street, New York, NY 10016.

Conception and Pregnancy

Booklet: 20pp. A factual account of how conception occurs, how a woman's body changes during pregnancy, and how the fetus develops. 50¢. New Readers Press, P.O. Box 131, Syracuse, NY 13210.

Education for Parenting

Book: 94pp. #108. By Mary B. Lane. The author relates her experiences in the Nurseries in Cross-Cultural Education (NICE) program to the broader needs of parents and children. Discusses the current status of parent education and provides alternatives for program development. Offers insights and understandings about work with parents. 1975. $3.00. National Association for the Education of Young Children, 1834 Connecticut Avenue N.W., Washington, DC 20009.

Giving Birth

Booklet: 28pp. Covers hospital and financial arrangements, labor and childbirth, prepared childbirth, anesthetics, premature birth, caesarean section, breastfeeding vs. bottlefeeding, and many practical details. 50¢. New Readers Press, P.O. Box 131, Syracuse, NY 13210.

Handbook for Home Care of Children

Book: 50pp, photos. #16. Useful to any mother providing day care in her home. Provides clear advice in easy to read print on how to handle the expected and the unexpected. Subjects include childhood growth, home safety, recipes for homemade art materials, and discipline. $1.50. Day Care and Child Development Council of America, 1012 Fourteenth Street N.W., Washington, DC 20005.

Having a Baby

Book: 168pp. Uncomplicated but reliable information on prenatal care, good nutrition, and infant care. Easy to read, with a sympathetic approach. $2.50. New Readers Press, P.O. Box 131, Syracuse, NY 13210.

Helping Your Child to Understand Death

Book: 64pp. By Anna W.M. Wolf. A thoughtful guide for helping children understand and accept death. Statements concerning the teachings and practices of the Jewish, Protestant, and Catholic faiths have been made in consultation with appropriate sources. 1973. $2.00 plus 50¢ for postage and service. Child Study Press, 50 Madison Avenue, New York, NY 10010.

Helping Your Handicapped Child

Booklet. Simple techniques for helping your handicapped child. Covers learning to dress, selecting clothes which are easy to put on, eating, grooming, and table manners. 28¢. New Readers Press, P.O. Box 131, Syracuse, NY 13210.

How to Help Your Child in School

Pamphlet. #381. By Robert Sunley. Emphasizes the many ways parents can help their children in school by stimulating their enthusiasm for learning. 35¢. Public Affairs Committee, Inc., 381 Park Avenue South, New York, NY 10016.

How to Organize an Effective Parent Group and Move Bureaucracies

Book: 112pp. #37. Discusses organization, leadership, lobbying, funding, coalitions, and relationships with professionals, students, and volunteers. Gives sample ads and press releases. Excellent handbook for action-oriented parents' groups, developed by a group of parents of handicapped children. $2.00. Day Care and Child Development Council of America, 1012 Fourteenth Street N.W., Washington, DC 20005.

Mothers at Work

Booklet: 16pp. Offers practical suggestions for working women, including arrangements for child care and home management. Discusses parent-child relationships, individual and family health and safety. Health and Welfare Division, Metropolitan Life Insurance Company, 1 Madison Avenue, New York, NY 10010.

Mothers in Paid Employment

Book: 140pp. #197. James Harrell and Peggy Pizzo, editors. Includes "Finding the Way to Love and Work—Reflections on the Question: Should Mothers Mother or Should Mothers Work?"; "Prospects and Patterns for Men and Women at Work: To Be Able Both to Love and to Work"; "The Parents of Small Children Need a Six-Hour Day"; "Employed Mothers and Their Families"; "Planning for Women in the Central City"; and "Public Policy and Working Mothers." $2.50. Day Care and Child Development Council of America, 1012 Fourteenth Street N.W., Washington, DC 20005.

Needs of Parents of Mentally Retarded Children

Pamphlet: 16pp. #65-3. By Mrs. Max A. Murray. The mother of a retarded child discusses the problems faced by parents and suggests how professionals can assist in their solution. 25¢. National Association for Retarded Citizens, P.O. Box 6109, Arlington, TX 76011.

Nueve Meses de Viaje

Leaflet: #9-0015. Spanish version of "Travel Time : 9 months." The National Foundation, March of Dimes, P.O. Box 2000, White Plains, NY 10602.

The Parent as Teacher

Book: 144pp. #ISBN-0-8224-5295-2. By D.H. Stott. A thought-provoking, sometimes startling analysis of learning disabilities by a distinguished educator who refuses to place the blame on lack of "intelligence," a concept he distrusts. Practical suggestions and proven methods of remediating learning disabilities make this book useful to both parent and teacher. 1974. $3.00. Fearon Publishers, Inc., 6 Davis Drive, Belmont, CA 94002.

Parent Involvement in Early Childhood Education

Book: 102pp. #135. By Alice S. Honig. An up-to-date account of programs working toward a more active involvement of the family with young children in positive interactions and learning experiences. Research, the rights of parents, ways to increase one's sensitivity and skills, and an extensive current resource list of materials and ideas are included. 1975. $3.00. National Association for the Education of Young Children, 1834 Connecticut Avenue N.W., Washington, DC 20009.

Parent Programs in Child Development Centers

Booklet: 85pp. #35. David L. Lillie, editor. Provides an overview of the needs of parent programs. Although written for special needs programs, the content is relevant to any new programs seeking rationale and direction in parent involvement. $2.00. Day Care and Child Development Council of America, 1012 Fourteenth Street N.W., Washington, DC 20005.

Parent's Guide to Child Discipline

Book: 112pp. By Rudolf Dreikurs and Loren Grey. This authoritative, easy-to-understand guide explains to parents why their children misbehave and shows how to deal with behavior problems. 1970. $2.95. Hawthorn Books, Inc., 260 Madison Avenue, New York, NY 10016.

Parents—Learn How Children Grow

Booklet: 32pp. Explains child growth and development from birth to early teens. Information on various ages permits parents to get an overall view. Specific suggestions about children's needs are made for each age level. 95¢. Moreno Educational Co., 7050 Belle Glade Lane, San Diego, CA 92119.

Parents' Responsibility

Booklet: 36pp. #244-06852. Designed to help parents and teachers tell the story of growth and development to young children. Revised 1970. $1.00. AAHPER Publications—Sales, 1201 Sixteenth Street N.W., Washington, DC 20036.

Parents—Teach Your Children to Learn

Booklet: 32pp. The major purpose of this booklet is to show that almost all parents can help develop the intelligence of their children. Gives specific recommendations for inexpensive, fun activities that can be carried on at home. 95¢. Moreno Educational Co., 7050 Belle Glade Lane, San Diego, CA 92119.

Parents—Your School Involvement Can Help Your Child

Booklet: 32pp. Explains the school setting and makes specific recommendations about parental involvement in the schools and how children can benefit from such involvement. The booklet provides space for parent's notes and school information. 95¢. Moreno Educational Co., 7050 Belle Glade Lane, San Diego, CA 92119.

Planning Your Family

Booklet: 16pp. Encourages the reader to begin thinking about family planning before marriage, describes both prescription and over-the-counter contraceptives, and calls attention to the drawbacks of other methods of birth control. 28¢. New Readers Press, P.O. Box 131, Syracuse, NY 13210.

Prenatal Care

Bulletin. #4-0116. Describes the newest developments in the care of high-risk infants and mothers before and after birth. The National Foundation, March of Dimes, P.O. Box 2000, White Plains, NY 10602.

Prenatal Care

Booklet: 24pp. Covers visits to the doctor or clinic, good nutrition, routine health care during pregnancy, minor problems, major problems and their danger signs, parenthood classes, and purchasing for the baby. 50¢. New Readers Press, P.O. Box 131, Syracuse, NY 13210.

Prenatal Care

Booklet: 6pp., #OP-57. Tells about the medical care needed during pregnancy. Describes abnormalities that the physician looks for. Gives suggestions on activities for the prospective mother. 15¢. American Medical Association, Health Education Materials, 535 North Dearborn Street, Chicago, IL 60610.

Preventing Mental Retardation

Booklet: 16pp. This booklet for prospective parents stresses avoidable or treatable causes of retardation: Rh factor, rubella, drugs, and poor nutrition during pregnancy; PKU; head injuries; poisoning from lead and other chemicals; and parental neglect. 28¢. New Readers Press, P.O. Box 131, Syracuse, NY 13210.

Primer for Parents of a Mentally Retarded Child

Pamphlet: 18pp. #10-12. By Elizabeth M. Stabler. Answers to questions often asked by parents who have just found out that they have a retarded child. Suitable for all members of the family. 25¢. National Association for Retarded Citizens, P.O. Box 6109, Arlington, TX 76011.

Protect Mommies from German Measles

Poster: 14" × 21". #9-0020. Urges parents to have their children vaccinated for rubella. The National Foundation, March of Dimes, P.O. Box 2000, White Plains, NY 10602.

Teaching Ideas for Parents
to Use with Their Children

Booklet: 32pp. Acquaints parents with teaching ideas they can use with their own children. Parents have always been excellent teachers of their children, but they can do even better if they use good teaching ideas. Gives vivid examples and concrete suggestions. 95¢. Moreno Educational Co., 7050 Belle Glade Lane, San Diego, CA 92119.

Tenga Buen Cuidado Su Bebe' Antes que Nazca.
Booklet. #9-0119. Spanish version of "Be Good to Your Baby before It Is Born." The National Foundation, March of Dimes, P.O. Box 2000, White Plains, NY 10602.

Three to Six: Your Child Starts to School
Booklet: #163. By James L. Hymes, Jr. For parents and those who work with children during the restless age—when children want to see, hear, feel, and know—and when they begin to attend school. 35¢. Public Affairs Committee, Inc., 381 Park Avenue South, New York, NY 10016.

Travel Time: 9 Months
Leaflet: #9-0016. Brief, authoritative pointers for the mother-to-be. The National Foundation, March of Dimes, P.O. Box 2000, White Plains, NY 10602.

T.V. or Not T.V.
Pamphlet: 4pp, cartoon illustrations in color. Entertaining and informative questions and answers about television viewing. Single copy free. American Optometric Association, 7000 Chippewa Street, St. Louis, MO 63119.

Vascular Birthmarks and Your Child
Booklet: 6pp. #OP-89. Analyzes three types of vascular birthmarks and discusses the outlook for their spontaneous disappearance. Explains when medical treatment is necessary. 15¢. American Medical Association, Health Education Materials, 535 Dearborn Street, Chicago, IL 60610.

What a Healthy Newborn Baby Looks Like
Reprint. #755. Description and life-size photo of a baby 5½ hours after birth. Of great interest to parents and prospective parents alike. Widely used for prenatal instruction by physicians

and nurses. 25¢. *Baby Talk* Magazine, 66 East Thirty-fourth Street, New York, NY 10016.

"What Can We Do Today, Mommy?"

Booklet. Parents' manual of preschool home experiences—easy, inexpensive things mothers or fathers can do with preschoolers at home. Provides brief suggestions to help parents become more sensitive to children's need to feel good about themselves. 90¢. Educational Research Council of America, Rockefeller Building, Cleveland, OH 44113.

What Should Parents Expect from Children?

Booklet. #357. By Jules Archer and Dixie Yahraes. Suggests how parents can work out standards of behavior with younger children and teenagers regarding family obligations and household chores. 35¢. Public Affairs Committee, Inc., 381 Park Avenue South, New York, NY 10016.

What to Do before Your Baby Comes

Booklet: 8pp. #OP-193. Written especially for the under-privileged mother to answer questions about pregnancy. 20¢. American Medical Association, Health Education Materials, 535 Dearborn Street, Chicago, IL 60610.

Whose Children?

Book: 118pp. A national report on the assistance needs of in-stitutionalized children. Gives special in-depth analyses of Texas and Washington, D.C. 1975. $1.50. The Children's Foundation, 1028 Connecticut Avenue N.W., Suite 1112, Washington, DC 20036.

Your Child—From Home to School

Booklet: 36pp. A handbook for parents whose child is entering school. $1.25. National School Public Relations Association, 1201 Sixteenth Street N.W., Washington, DC 20036.

Psychology

(See also Guidance)

Black Is a Word

Booklet: 30pp. A discussion of race for the young and for adults. $1.10. Pacific Education Publications, Inc., 2121 McKinley Street, Honolulu, HI 96822.

The Challenge of Child Training

Book: 160pp. By Rudolf Dreikurs. Provides practical advice on specific situations, from weaning to classroom difficulties. Explores the reasons behind children's behavior, discusses the most common mistakes in child training, and describes the most effective methods of training. 1972. $2.95. Hawthorn Books, Inc., 260 Madison Avenue, New York, NY 10016.

Children and Drugs

Bulletin: 64pp. Offers guidelines to teachers working with drug-using children, plus suggestions on working with their parents. 1972. $2.50. Association for Childhood Education International, 3615 Wisconsin Avenue N.W., Washington, DC 20016.

Children and TV—
Television's Impact on the Child

Book: 64pp. Thirteen stimulating contributions look at program content, what TV teaches, use and abuse of the medium, guidance by parents, and TV as curriculum. 1967. $1.25. Association for Childhood Education International, 3615 Wisconsin Avenue N.W., Washington, DC 20016.

Children and War

Leaflet: 8pp. A position paper by Norma R. Law. Contains excerpts from children's writings and statistics from a survey of children and their teachers. Rejects killing; gives ways to educate for peace. 1973. 35¢. Association for Childhood Education International, 3615 Wisconsin Avenue N.W., Washington, DC 20016.

Children's Views of Themselves

Bulletin: 40pp. By Ira J. Gordon. A lively, sympathetic look at children through new eyes and deepened perception of their feelings and ego-building needs. Suggests how adults can develop sensitivity to children. 1972. $2.00. Association for Childhood Education International, 3615 Wisconsin Avenue N.W., Washington, DC 20016.

Coping with Children's Misbehavior: A Parent's Guide

Book: 162pp. By Rudolf Dreikurs. Discusses why a child misbehaves and gives modern, efficient methods for dealing with trying situations, including temper tantrums, poor performance at school, and many others. 1972. $2.95. Hawthorn Books, Inc., 260 Madison Avenue, New York, NY 10016.

Help! These Kids Are Driving Me Crazy

Book: 120pp. #0062. By Dr. Ronald D. Carter. In light, nontechnical language, teaches the methods and humane practice of behavior modification. $3.50. Research Press, P.O. Box 31779, Champaign, IL 61820.

Helping Your Child to Understand Death

Book: 64pp. By Anna W.M. Wolf. A thoughtful guide for helping children understand and accept death. Statements concerning the teachings and practices of the Jewish, Protestant, and Catholic faiths have been made in consultation with appropriate sources. 1973. $2.00 plus 50¢ for postage and service. Child Study Press, 50 Madison Avenue, New York, NY 10010.

Home Token Economy

Kit: guide and 10 charts. #1069. Introduces a program of predetermined tasks to be performed in order to achieve reward. A new pattern of family life can be established for the benefit of all family members. $2.50. Research Press, P.O. Box 31779, Champaign, IL 61820.

Living with Children
Booklet: 112pp. #0003. Utilizes an effective programmed format that changes the behavior of the reader by giving skills which can be used immediately. $3.50. Research Press, P.O. Box 31779, Champaign, IL 61820.

Modifying Classroom Behavior
Book: 104pp. #0089. By Nancy K. Buckley. A basic resource for teachers who want to strengthen the motivation of their students. Emphasizes a positive rather than punitive approach, demonstrating persuasively that negative activities can be diminished as classroom success is increased. $3.60. Research Press, P.O. Box 31779, Champaign, IL 61820.

Pain and Joy in School
Book: 88pp. #0488. Increases teacher sensitivity and reminds adults who work with children that unless they are very well-adjusted individuals, they are quite capable of inflicting deep pain on a child. $3.00 Research Press, P.O. Box 31779, Champaign, IL 61820.

Schizophrenia:
Current Approaches to a Baffling Problem
Booklet. #460. By Arthur Henley. Describes the symptoms and treatments of this condition, as well as theories about it. More than two million Americans—and perhaps as many as five million—suffer from various forms of this baffling mental disorder. 35¢. Public Affairs Committee, Inc., 381 Park Avenue South, New York, NY 10016.

Teaching Social Behavior to Young Children
Book: 96pp. #0631. Explains the principles and practice of behavioral supervision clearly in real-life situations. $3.50. Research Press, P.O. Box 31779, Champaign, IL 61820.

When Children Need Special Help with Emotional Problems

Pamphlet: 30pp. By Greta Mayer and Mary Hoover. A thoughtful guide for helping parents and teachers recognize and get treatment for children's problems that need special consideration. Discusses the questions: How does one tell when a problem requires professional help? How and where does one find help? $1.25 plus 50¢ for postage and service. Child Study Press, 50 Madison Avenue, New York, NY 10010.

Who Am I? The Development of Self-Concept

Booklet: 16pp, illustrated. #55. By Dorothy J. Kiester. "If we can help our children develop sturdy self-concepts with healthy faith in themselves, maybe they will manage their own and society's future better than we could hope for in any other way." Explores self-concept and ways to help its development. $2.00. Day Care and Child Development Council of America, 1012 Fourteenth Street N.W., Washington, DC 20005.

Your Child's Emotional Health

Booklet. #264. By Anna W.M. Wolf. Provides guidance on handling overaggressive and underaggressive children, hidden fears and anxieties, and family crises such as financial troubles, illness, death, and marriage problems. 35¢. Public Affairs Committee, Inc., 381 Park Avenue South, New York, NY 10016.

Reading

Animated Enrichment Texts— A Child's Concept Alphabet*

Book: 56pp. #4030. The teacher introduces one letter per week, and the child associates definitions and concepts with each letter. Activities and readings are suggested for each unit. Uses cartoon characters. $1.95. Instructional Fair, Inc., 4158 Lake Michigan Drive, Grand Rapids, MI 49504.

I Read . . . I See. . . . I Hear. . . . I Learn

Book. #8389-3124-3. Also available in Spanish. For four age groups: preschool, 5 to 8, 9 to 11, and 12 to 14. Lists books, films, records, and stories for each group. $2.00. Order Dept., American Library Association, 50 East Huron Street, Chicago, IL 60611.

Long Vowel Sounds

Book: 128pp. Twenty-one lessons present the long vowel sounds and the regular spellings for each. The student learns that a long vowel sound may be spelled in several ways. $2.00. New Readers Press, P.O. Box 131, Syracuse, NY 13210.

Prereading Experiences

Booklet: 40pp. #5045. Sections one and two present lesson plans for prereading experiences, questions, ideas, and vocabulary development. Section three lists sequenced skills in behavioral terms and suggests methods. Section four lists equipment and manipulative materials and gives the concepts and motor skills developed in a multi-sensory approach. $1.95. Instructional Fair, Inc., 4158 Lake Michigan Drive, Grand Rapids, MI 49504.

Reading Aloud to Children

Brochure: 6pp. #8389-509-1. Gives helpful suggestions on conducting a program of reading aloud to children. Contains a short bibliography. 16¢ plus a self-addressed mailing label. Order Dept., American Library Association, 50 East Huron Street, Chicago, IL 60611.

Reading Bulletin Boards

Booklet: 48pp. #368. Nearly fifty displays: motivational devices, decoding skills, vocabulary, and study skills. $1.95. The Instructor Publications, Inc., Dansville, NY 14437.

Reading Takes Seeing

Leaflet: 4pp. Emphasizes the importance of good vision to reading. Single copy free. Public Information Division, American Optometric Association, 7000 Chippewa Street, St. Louis, MO 63119.

Reading with Your Child through Age 5

Booklet: 48pp, illustrated. A guide to selecting books to read aloud to young children. Contains annotated listings of more than 200 books, covering a variety of subjects and ethnic groups. 1976. $1.50 plus 50¢ for service and postage. Child Study Press, 50 Madison Avenue, New York, NY 10010.

Short Vowel Sounds

Book: 80pp. Contains fifteen lessons structured around the short vowels and the sounds they represent. Introduces various vowel and consonant combinations, as well as some consonant blends. Emphasizes word recognition through the use of phonic skills. $1.60. New Readers Press, P.O. Box 131, Syracuse, NY 13210.

Sounds and Names of Letters*

Book: 72pp. Begins on a zero level, so it can be used by a person who cannot read any letters or words. The first five lessons contain picture association charts to teach the key words and sounds, a story using the key words, a writing lesson, and a homework page. Lessons six to eleven present key words, letters, and numbers. $1.40. New Readers Press, P.O. Box 131, Syracuse, NY 13210.

Your Child and Reading: How You Can Help

Booklet: 14pp. Gives ideas on how parents can help their children learn to read and become interested in books. 21¢. Houghton-Mifflin Co., 1900 South Batavia Avenue, Geneva, IL 60134.

Recreation and Physical Education

(See also Motor Development)

Best Records and Books for Physical Education for the Elementary Grades

Catalog: 20pp. Lists records and books available for physical education. All materials have been carefully tested by experts for quality and relevance to the needs and interests of today's young people. Single copy free. Children's Music Center, 5373 West Pico Boulevard, Los Angeles, CA 90019.

Best Records, Books, and Instruments for Dance and Dance Therapy

Catalog: 48pp. Single copy free. Children's Music Center, 5373 West Pico Boulevard, Los Angeles, CA 90019.

Desirable Athletic Competition for Children of Elementary School Age

Booklet: 36pp. #241-07964. A report of research on the effects of competition on young children, with recommendations for school-sponsored athletic competition. 1968. $1.25. AAHPER Publications—Sales, 1201 Sixteenth Street N.W., Washington, DC 20036.

Essentials of a Quality Elementary School Physical Education Program

Position paper. #245-25022. A position statement covering teacher preparation, instructional programs, evaluation time allotment, class size, teaching load, dress, equipment and facilities, and school-related programs. 75¢. AAHPER Publications—Sales, 1201 Sixteenth Street N.W., Washington, DC 20036.

Game Time Obstacle Course Stunts

Pamphlet: 27pp. Includes directions for stunts on turning bar, high parallel bars, low parallel bars, balance beam, climbing fence, tunnel, horizontal ladder, hurdle, and dodge posts. Game Time, 900 Anderson Road, Litchfield, MI 49252.

Open Space Learning Place
Booklet. By Robin Moore. Discusses open space learning places. Useful to teachers and others involved in developing play areas. $1.00. New School of Education Journal, 4304 Tolman Hall, University of California, Berkeley, CA 94720.

Outdoor Education
Booklet: 32pp. #246-07320. Gives statements of values and examples of activities and projects in outdoor education for the elementary school. 1970. $1.50. AAHPER Publications—Sales, 1201 Sixteenth Street N.W., Washington, DC 20036.

Physical Education
for Children's Healthful Living
Bulletin: 80pp. Supports the importance of movement as a way of learning. Describes quality environments, good programs, safety education, and formulas for play. Bibliography. 1968. $1.50. Association for Childhood Education International, 3615 Wisconsin Avenue N.W., Washington, DC 20016.

Physical Growth Chart for Boys*
Chart. #244-06960. Profile chart for recording height and weight. For use in both elementary and secondary schools. 15¢ each. AAHPER Publications—Sales, 1201 Sixteenth Street N.W., Washington, DC 20036.

Physical Growth Chart for Girls*
Chart. #244-06962. Profile chart for recording height and weight. For use in both elementary and secondary schools. 15¢ each. AAHPER Publications—Sales, 1201 Sixteenth Street N.W., Washington, DC 20036.

Rhythmic Activities for the Classroom
Booklet: 48pp. #376. A guide to teaching rhythmic movement and dance. $1.95. The Instructor Publications, Inc., Dansville, NY 14437.

Swimming for the Handicapped Child and Adult

Leaflet: 13pp. #B-42. By Lou Neishloss. Discusses the benefits of swimming and gives tips to help the instructor teach swimming to persons with various kinds of disabilities. 1973. 25¢. National Easter Seal Society for Crippled Children and Adults, 2023 West Odgen Avenue, Chicago, IL 60612.

Trends in Elementary School Physical Education

Reprint: 24pp. #245-25122. A series of recent articles interpreting new developments and promising practices concerning the role of physical education in learning, movement education, and teacher preparation. 1970. 75¢. AAHPER Publications—Sales, 1201 Sixteenth Street N.W., Washington, DC 20036.

Your Child's Health and Fitness

Pamphlet: 16pp. #242-06774. Reviews the *what* and *why* of physical fitness. Written for parents as well as teachers; suitable for parent-teacher meetings. 15¢. AAHPER Publications—Sales, 1201 Sixteenth Street N.W., Washington, DC 20036.

Safety

(See also Audiovisual)

Danger Lurks

Card: 8½" × 11". #OP0304. For the medicine cabinet. Contains information on what to do in case of accidental poisoning. 20¢. American Medical Association, Health Education Materials, 535 Dearborn Street, Chicago, IL 60610.

Let's Learn about Safety

Pamphlet. Discusses safety with tools, medicines, cars, and when swimming. Available free to Head Start and early childhood programs; requests should be made on school letterhead. Public Relations Services Department, Eli Lilly and Company, 307 East McCarty Street, Indianapolis, IN 46206.

Meet Seymour Safely*

Kit. A complete vision education program for primary-grade children that helps teach the importance of vision care at an early age. The 32-page booklet offers pages of Seymour Safely puppet skits, songs, jingles, games, and puppet patterns. Each kit also contains a Seymour Safely puppet and other pamphlets and brochures. $1.00. Public Information Division, American Optometric Association, 7000 Chippewa Street, St. Louis, MO 63119.

Protecting Your Family
from Accidental Poisoning

Pamphlet. #459. By Arthur S. Freese. Nearly two million children and many adults in the U.S. are endangered by accidental poisoning every year. Pinpoints the hazards and suggests preventive measures and emergency care. Discusses poisoning from medicines, household products, food, lead, and mercury. 35¢. Public Affairs Committee, Inc., 381 Park Avenue South, New York, NY 10016.

Safe Toys for Your Child:
How to Select Them, How to Use Them Safely

Booklet: 8pp. #473. Tells parents how to select safe toys for children. Includes information on the care of children's toys and on safety legislation. 1971. 35¢. Superintendent of Documents, U.S. Government Printing Office, Washington, DC 20402.

Safety Theme*
Set. #07013. Acquaints children with safety rules and practices. Encourages safety habits and caution in everyday life at home, at play, and at school. The set has twelve pictures in full color along with twelve convenient resource sheets detailing facts to know, questions to ask, suggested aims, things to do, learning activities, and other resources. $3.75. David C. Cook Publishing Co., School Products Division, 850 North Grove Avenue, Elgin, IL 60120.

Teacher's Packet on Children's Eye Safety
Packet. #620. A guide to teaching eye safety in the early primary grades. Includes spirit masters for classroom activities. Kentucky Society for the Prevention of Blindness, 301 Heyburn Building, Louisville, KY 40202.

Teaching Safety in the Elementary School
Booklet: #244-25384. A revision of AAHPER's popular booklet for classroom teachers and professional preparation courses. Presents general safety information for teachers, methods for teaching safety, and sources of additional information and safety teaching aids. $2.25. AAHPER Publications— Sales, 1201 Sixteenth Street N.W., Washington, DC 20036.

Tetanus—The Second Deadliest Poison
Pamphlet: 8pp. #OP-18. Tells how scratches can lead to tetanus. Explains the dangers of tetanus. 15¢. American Medical Association, Health Education Materials, 525 Dearborn Street, Chicago, IL 60610.

Your Child's Safety
Booklet: 28pp. Contains information on children's growth and development patterns which can help parents to foresee potential accident situations and take precautions. Emphasizes the importance of safe surroundings, play space, and play materials. Health and Welfare Division, Metropolitan Life Insurance Company, 1 Madison Avenue, New York, NY 10010.

Science

Green Thumb Activities for Classroom Gardeners

Booklet: 48pp. #311. Classroom activities with seeds and plants: propagation, outdoor gardening, items for gifts, and more. $1.95. The Instructor Publications, Inc., Dansville, NY 14437.

Let's Collect Shells and Rocks

Booklet: 21pp. Provides basic information about rock and shell collecting. Shell Oil Company, 1 Shell Plaza, P.O. Box 2463, Houston, TX 77001.

The Little Seed That Grew and Grew*

Poster. This colorful poster describes the growing of the avocado seed. May be used to stimulate creativity in science. California Avocado Advisory Board News, 4533-B MacArthur Boulevard, Newport Beach, CA 92660.

Plants and Seeds*

Set. #30700. Introduces and explains concepts of the natural world. Illustrates how plants start, grow, and live. Stimulates discussion and encourages questions. Twelve pictures and twelve resource sheets with facts, learning activities, rhythmic activities, stories, and other resources. $3.75. David C. Cook Publishing Co., School Products Division, 850 North Grove Avenue, Elgin, IL 60120.

Science Studies*

Flannelgraph kit. #06841. Fifty-six full-color flannelgraph pictures of squirrels, peanuts, cotton, and so on. Twenty-four-page booklet provides actual samples, information, ideas, stories, rhythmic activities, and more. $3.50. David C. Cook Publishing Co., School Products Division, 850 North Grove Avenue, Elgin, IL 60120.

Science Themes*
Set. #07211. Dramatizes basic science concepts with twelve full-color pictures and twelve resource sheets. $3.75. David C. Cook Publishing Co., School Products Division, 850 North Grove Avenue, Elgin, IL 60120.

Science Themes II*
Set. #30643. Additional scientific concepts on twelve full-color pictures with resource sheets. $3.75. David C. Cook Publishing Co., School Products Division, 850 North Grove Avenue, Elgin, IL 60120.

Seasons*
Set. #06999. Helps children enjoy the changing seasons and understand the responses and adjustments of animals, plants, and people to the rhythms of nature. Twelve pictures and twelve resource sheets complete with facts, suggested aims, questions, things to do, and rhythmic activities. $3.75. David C. Cook Publishing Co., School Products Division, 850 North Grove Avenue, Elgin, IL 60120.

Seasons and Weather*
Flannelboard packet. #24190. Helps children become aware of daily and seasonal changes. Nineteen pictures, record with six songs, resource sheets. $3.75. David C. Cook Publishing Co., School Products Division, 850 North Grove Avenue, Elgin, IL 60120.

Sex Education

How to Tell Your Child about Sex
Pamphlet. #149. By James L. Hymes, Jr. Points out questions children commonly ask and suggests what parents should say and when they should say it. 35¢. Public Affairs Committee, Inc., 381 Park Avenue South, New York, NY 10016.

The Miracle of Growth*

Book. Compiled by the Chicago Museum of Science and the University of Illinois. A simple but comprehensive account of conception, birth, and development from infancy to adolescence, giving special attention to heredity. For the early elementary school age child. 1967. $4.95; paper, $1.75. University of Illinois Press, Urbana, IL 61801.

What to Tell Your Child about Sex

Book: 97pp. The classic guide, in question-and-answer form, to what children need to know at each age from infancy through adolescence. 1974. $2.50 (paper, $1.50) plus 50¢ for postage and service. Child Study Press, 50 Madison Avenue, New York, NY 10010.

When Children Ask about Sex

Booklet: 42pp. By Ada Daniels and Mary Hoover. A guide for parents. Explains that sexual development is part of a child's total growth and that questions about sex should be answered honestly in terms appropriate to the child's age and needs. 1974. $1.25 plus 50¢ for postage and service. Child Study Press, 50 Madison Avenue, New York, NY 10010.

Transportation

A Freight Train Comes to My House*

Leaflet. A storybook for young children to learn about trains. Includes learning exercises. Association of American Railroads, Office of Information and Public Affairs, 1920 L Street N.W., Washington, DC 20036.

Railroads in Our Daily Lives

Leaflet. A teacher's manual for the primary grades. Association of American Railroads, Office of Information and Public Affairs, 1920 L Street N.W., Washington, DC 20036.

Transportation*

Set. #30635. Deals with ways of transporting people and materials by land, water, and air. Covers safety rules, equipment, and the many workers needed. An exciting panorama of modern transportation. Twelve full-color pictures plus twelve resource sheets giving suggested aims, questions, facts, activities, background, and stories. $3.75. David C. Cook Publishing Co., School Products Division, 850 North Grove Avenue, Elgin, IL 60120.